CALIFORNIA
Interactive Reading Notepad: Inquiry Companion

MAGRUDER'S
AMERICAN GOVERNMENT

SAVVAS
LEARNING COMPANY

ISBN-13: 978-1-41-828735-1
ISBN-10:   1-41-828735-0
ScoutAutomatedPrintCode   11 22

Contents

California Magruder's American Government
Interactive Reading Notepad: Inquiry Companion

Lesson 1.1 Principles of Government

Key Terms

government

public policies

legislative power

executive power

judicial power

dictatorship

democracy

Aristotle

state

sovereign

Thomas Hobbes

John Locke

Academic Vocabulary

fundamental: basic, essential primary

populous: having a large population

personnel: people who work for an organization

administration: a performance of duties

abundant: available in large quantity, plentiful

maxim: a general truth or rule of conduct

Lesson Objectives

1 **Define** government and the basic powers every government holds.

2 **Describe** the four defining characteristics of a state.

3 **Identify** the four theories that attempt to explain the origin of the state.

4 **Understand** the purpose of government in the United States and other countries.

Government—We The People

1. **Identify Supporting Details** As you read "Government: We The People" draw a 3-circle Venn Diagram to show how the three basic powers possessed by all governments combine to make up a government. For each power, insert an example.

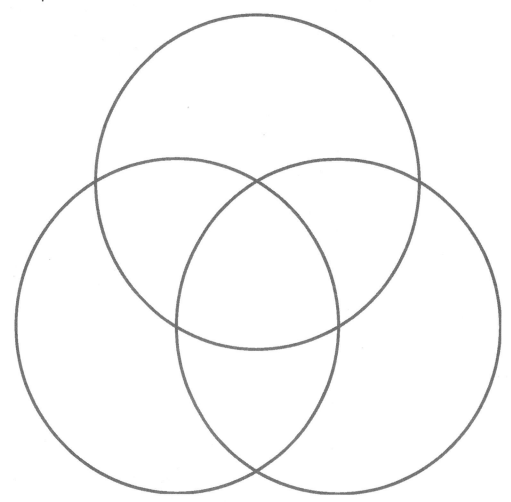

2. **Compare and Contrast** How is a government conducted under a dictatorship? How does a dictatorship different from a democracy?

3. **Vocabulary: Read Context Clues** Read the paragraph that first mentions Aristotle. What do you think the word *political* means in the sentence? Why did Aristotle use that word in his writing? Use evidence from the text to support your answer.

The State

4. **Define** What is patriotism? Give an example.

5. **Identify Cause and Effect** Read the discussion of Thomas Hobbes's ideas about why states need government. Why did Thomas Hobbes consider government necessary? Use the text to support your answer.

6. **Describe** What is the difference between a state and a nation?

How States Arose

7. **Cite Evidence** Read the paragraphs about the social contract theory. Cite evidence from the Declaration of Independence that shows that the signers believed in this theory.

8. **Draw Conclusions** Review the section of text that discusses the historical development of governments and describes the four theories of the origin of the state. Which two theories do you think a dictator might claim as justification for taking power? Why?

What Government Does

9. **Determine Central Ideas** Why is a written constitution important for governing a state?

10. **Identify Cause and Effect** How does widespread access to education promote the general welfare?

Lesson 1.2 Types of Government

Key Terms

autocracy

oligarchy

unitary government

federal government

division of powers

confederation

presidential government

parliamentary

Abraham Lincoln

Alexander Pope

Academic Vocabulary

concise: brief; to the point

canton: a local governmental unit in Switzerland

regimes: particular governments

prestige: a reputation based on achievement

elite: a select group, a privileged class

coequal: having the same standing before the law

Lesson Objectives

1 **Classify** governments according to three sets of characteristics.

2 **Define** systems of government based on who can participate.

3 **Identify** different ways that power can be distributed, geographically, within a state.

4 **Describe** a government by the distribution of power between the executive branch and legislative branch.

Classifying Governments

1. **Draw Inferences** Why is geographical distribution of power important in the United States?

2. **Draw Conclusions** Why is the relationship between the executive and legislative branches a useful way to classify governments?

Who Can Participate?

3. **Make Comparisons** How does the U.S. constitutional republic compare to authoritarian forms of government?

4. **Contrast** What characteristics does a theocracy have that are missing in the U.S. constitutional republic form of government? Explain.

Geographic Distribution of Power

5. **Synthesize** Analyze the advantages and disadvantages of the federal, confederate, and unitary systems of government. Include at least two advantages and two disadvantages of each system in the table below.

System of Government	Advantages	Disadvantages
Federal		
Unitary		
Confederate		

Interactive Reading Notepad • Lesson 1.2

6. **Cite Evidence** While there are three ways to classify government (the number of persons who can participate, where power resides, and the relationship between the executive and legislative branches), many people find it most useful to classify governments by the number of people who can participate in the government. Why do you think this is so? Cite evidence from the text to support your answer.

Legislative and Executive Powers

7. **Determine Central Ideas** How is the executive branch related to the legislative branch in a presidential government?

8. **Analyze** Analyze the advantages and disadvantages of parliamentary systems of government.

Lesson 1.3 Origins of the Democratic Modern State

Key Terms

patricians

plebeians

feudalism

sovereignty

legitimacy

divine right of kings

colonialism

mercantilism

François-Marie Arouet

William Blackstone

Academic Vocabulary

extinguish: end, destroy

epochal event: a notable happening that marks the beginning of an era

catalyst: something that prompts, brings about change

guild: association of craftsmen or merchants

charismatic: having personal appeal and attractiveness

monopolize: prevent others from sharing; control, dominate

Lesson Objectives

1 **Identify** the ancient foundations of the state in Athens, in Rome, and in the feudal system.

2 **Analyze** the rise of sovereign states.

3 **Understand** why European nations turned to colonialism.

4 **Explain** how governments can achieve legitimacy.

5 **Understand** how Enlightenment ideas helped influence the expansion of popular sovereignty.

Building on the Past

1. **Compare and Contrast** How were the governments of ancient Athens and the Roman Republic similar? How were they different?

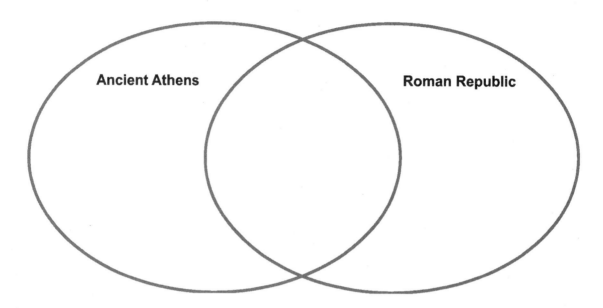

2. **Identify Supporting Details** What aspects of government did the Roman Republic share with a true democracy?

3. **Draw Inferences** Why do you think serfs accepted their position at the bottom of the feudal pyramid?

Nations and Kings

4. **Identify Cause and Effect** What impact did the Black Plague have on the rise of mercantilism?

5. **Determine Meaning of Words** What do you think the term *absolute monarchy* means? What impact did absolute monarchy have on monarchs' ability to establish governments?

Power, Authority, and Legitimacy

6. **Summarize** What approaches are used by rulers to gain legitimacy?

Europe Colonizes the World

7. **Use Visual Information** Based on the map provided, describe the system of trade among European nations and their colonies.

8. **Determine Central Ideas** What was the ultimate goal that drove monarchs to colonize and to establish international trade routes?

Power Comes from the People

9. **Paraphrase** In your own words, describe the philosophies of the Baron de Montesquieu and John Locke.

10. **Explain an Argument** Explain Blackstone's concept of common law.

Lesson 1.4 The Basics of Democracy

Key Terms

majority rule	Winston Churchill
compromise	Oliver Wendell Holmes, Jr.
citizen	Theodore Roosevelt
free enterprise system	George Washington
James Bryce	

Academic Vocabulary

subordinate: of lesser rank

arbitrary: based on unsupported opinion, random choice

inevitable: unavoidable, sure to happen

adequate: enough to meet the needs of a situation

initiative: enterprise, resourcefulness

antitrust laws: laws that regulate business practices in order to promote competition

zoning ordinances: laws that regulate the uses of property in certain areas

---

Lesson Objectives

1 **Understand** the foundations of democracy.

2 **Analyze** the connections between democracy and the free enterprise system.

Foundations of Democracy

1. **Summarize** Use the chart to list the five basic notions of democracy. Then explain what each means to a U.S. citizen.

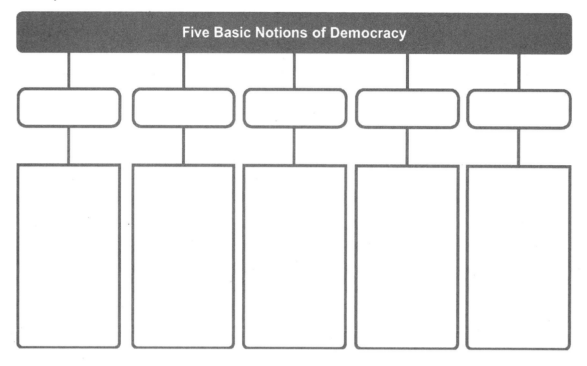

Five Basic Notions of Democracy

2. **Paraphrase** Explain the concept of *majority rule* in your own words.

3. **Compare and Contrast** Compare and contrast the following two quotations from the text:

> "The right to swing my fist ends where the other man's nose begins."
>
> —Justice Oliver Wendell Holmes
>
> and
>
> "The rights of every man are diminished when the rights of one man are threatened."
>
> —John F. Kennedy

Responsibilities, Duties, and Obligations of Citizenship

4. **Determine Central Ideas** Theodore Roosevelt said: "The first requisite of a good citizen in our republic is that he should be able and willing to pull his weight." What does this mean to a U.S. citizen?

Democracy and The Free Enterprise System

5. **Use Visual Information** Look at the art that illustrates the concept of capitalism and the free enterprise system. The second pillar is labeled *Individual Initiative*. Considering that the word *initiative* means "the energy and desire that is needed to do something," what do you think *individual initiative* means? According to the drawing, how does it relate to capitalism?

6. **Draw Conclusions** What is government's role in the free enterprise system?

Lesson 2.1 Origins of American Political Ideals

Key Terms

limited government

representative government

Magna Carta

due process

Petition of Right

English Bill of Rights

charter

bicameral

proprietary

unicameral

Jamestown

King John

King Charles I

William and Mary of Orange

Glorious Revolution

King George II

George Calvert, Lord Baltimore

William Penn

Academic Vocabulary

landmark: historical, pivotal, highly significant

arbitrary: not restrained or limited in the exercise of power

venture: an undertaking involving risk

levy: to impose, to collect by legal authority

haven: a place of safety

Lesson Objectives

1 **Identify** how constitutional government in the United States was influenced by key ideas that were developed over centuries in England and elsewhere.

2 **Explain** the significance of three landmark English documents to the American system of government.

3 **Describe** the three types of colonies that the English established in North America and why they are important to the study of American government.

Origins of American Constitutional Government

1. **Determine Central Ideas** What were three basic concepts of government that the English brought with them to North America? How did these concepts influence constitutional government in America?

Influential Documents and Ideas

2. **Compare and Contrast** How are the Petition of Right and the English Bill of Rights similar? How are they different? Cite examples from the text to support your answer.

3. **Summarize** How are the notions of ordered, limited, and representative government reflected in the three landmark documents? Cite examples from each document.

Three Types of Colonies

4. **Identify Supporting Details** As you read "Three Types of Colonies," use this graphic organizer to record characteristics of each type of colony.

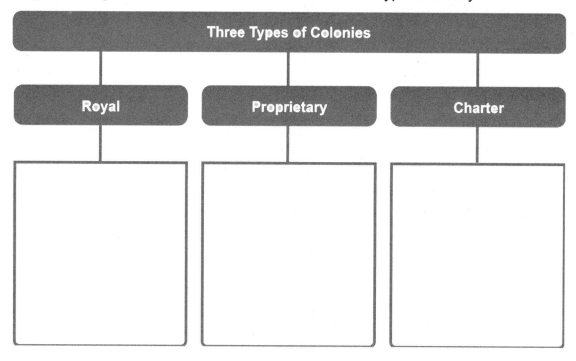

5. **Identify Cause and Effect** In what ways do you think the "stern hand" of the royal governors affected colonists' feelings toward the Crown?

6. **Use Visual Information** Look at the image of the "Charter Oak Tree," and read the caption that accompanies it. What does this information suggest about the feelings of the colonists in the time leading up to the Revolution?

7. **Summarize** How was the system of government different in the charter colonies than in the royal colonies? How did these differences impact the future of these colonies? Use supporting details from the text to support your answer.

Lesson 2.2 Independence

Key Terms

confederation

Albany Plan of Union

delegates

duty

popular sovereignty

Samuel Adams

Roger Sherman

John Jay

George Washington

John Adams

James Wilson

Thomas Jefferson

John Locke

Academic Vocabulary

repeal: to cancel

boycott: a refusal to buy or sell certain goods

ablest: the most talented, capable, competent, skillful

unalienable: cannot be surrendered or transferred; sacred

Lesson Objectives

1 **Explain** how Britain's colonial policies contributed to the growth of self-government in the colonies.

2 **Identify** the major steps that led to growing feelings of colonial unity.

3 **Consider** the ways that the colonists organized against British policies as well as the contributions of significant individuals, including Thomas Jefferson, Samuel Adams, John Adams, Roger Sherman, John Jay, and George Washington.

4 **Examine** the debates and compromises that impacted the creation of the Declaration of Independence.

5 **Understand** the major ideas of the Declaration of Independence, including unalienable rights, the social contract theory, and the right of resistance to illegitimate government.

British Colonial Policies

1. **Determine Central Ideas** The colonies provided England with raw materials for manufacturing. By the mid-1700s, what did England provide to the colonies?

2. **Analyze Interactions** Each colonial legislature operated fairly independently from England. Explain one way that these legislatures could exercise control over their royal governors.

3. **Identify Cause and Effect** Why did King George III change the way England ruled the colonies? Why did the colonists object?

Interactive Reading Notepad • Lesson 2.2

Growing Colonial Unity

4. **Identify Cause and Effect** Think about why the colonies cooperated with each other. List one reason why each of the following was formed or took place.

 – **New England Confederation**

 – **Albany meeting**

 – **Stamp Act Congress**

 – **Committees of Correspondence**

5. **Predict Consequences** Why might these forms of cooperation have helped the colonists after they declared independence?

6. **Assess an Argument** The colonists objected to "taxation without representation." What kind of taxation do you think they would have supported? Why?

First Continental Congress

7. **Assess an Argument** In 1774, Parliament called the actions of the Boston Tea Party "dangerous commotions and insurrections" and responded by closing the Boston Harbor and preventing town meetings in Massachusetts. Why did the colonists call these two decrees part of the "Intolerable Acts" and set up a meeting to discuss a response?

8. **Draw Inferences** Two of the "Intolerable Acts" affected Massachusetts only. Why did other colonies care about what happened there?

9. **Draw Conclusions** Why did the First Continental Congress send a Declaration of Rights to King George III instead of declaring war against England?

10. **Analyze Interactions** Why did the First Continental Congress encourage a boycott? How would a boycott be an effective action against Britain? Why did Congress need local committees to enforce it?

Second Continental Congress

11. **Determine Central Ideas** List five responsibilities of the Second Continental Congress as the acting government of the colonies.

12. **Compare and Contrast** Think about the work undertaken by the Second Continental Congress. Name one way that it differed from the work of the First Continental Congress.

The Declaration of Independence

13. **Draw Conclusions** Why was there spirited debate about Richard Henry Lee's resolution that "these United Colonies are, and of right ought to be, free and Independent States"?

14. **Determine Meaning** Look at the text of the Declaration of Independence. According to this document, why are governments created?

15. **Determine Central Ideas** What made the political system described in the Declaration of Independence groundbreaking?

16. **Draw Inferences** How did the Declaration of Independence change the meaning of the 1775 battles of Lexington and Concord?

The First State Constitutions

17. **Analyze Sequence** Why did individual colonies begin replacing their royal charters with State constitutions before the Declaration of Independence?

18. **Determine Meaning** List the five most common features of the State governments created in 1776 and 1777. Pick one of these features, and write a definition using your own words.

19. **Integrate Information from Diverse Sources** What features of the first State constitutions were similar to ideas expressed in the Declaration of Independence?

20. **Draw Conclusions** Why did the first State constitutions seek to limit government power?

Lesson 2.3 First Steps

Key Terms

Articles of Confederation
ratification
full faith and credit
Shays' Rebellion

Daniel Shays
Alexander Hamilton
James Madison

Academic Vocabulary

jurisdiction: legal authority
presiding officer: the chair of a meeting
arsenal: a store of arms or military equipment

Lesson Objectives

1 **Describe** the debates that impacted the creation of the Articles of Confederation, the structure of the government set up under the Articles, and how that government was influenced by ideas, people, and historical documents.

2 **Explain** why the weaknesses of the Articles led to a critical period for the country in the 1780s.

3 **Describe** how a growing need for a stronger national government led to plans for a Constitutional Convention.

The Articles of Confederation

1. **Summarize** Summarize the key debates that delayed approval of the Articles of Confederation and why these issues were important to the colonists.

2. **Identify Supporting Details** The government established by the Articles was quite simple. Outline its basic structure.

3. **Cite Evidence** What evidence can you find in the text to support the idea that the Articles of Confederation sought to protect the independence of the States rather than to create a strong central government?

4. **Determine Central Ideas** In what ways did the States agree to support the Articles of Confederation? Why did Congress depend on this support in order to be effective?

A Time of Troubles, the 1780s

5. **Identify Cause and Effect** As you read "A Time of Troubles, the 1780s," use this graphic organizer to record the actions the States were able to take as a result of the weaknesses of the Articles.

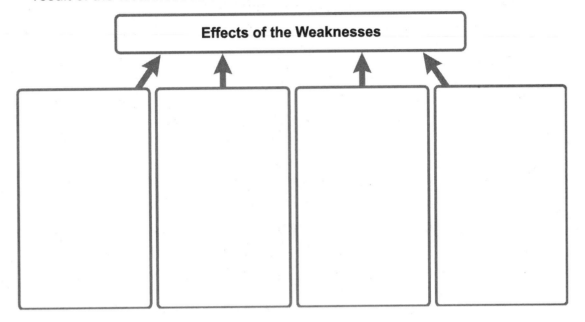

6. **Identify Cause and Effect** Explain how features of the Articles of Confederation led to the currency disaster that occurred following the Revolutionary War.

7. **Vocabulary: Determine Meaning** In late 1786, George Washington wrote the following: "It is but the other day that we were shedding our blood to obtain the Constitutions under which we now live—Constitutions of our own choice and making—and now we are unsheathing the sword to overturn them."

   To what Constitutions is Washington referring? What event is he referencing when he talks about "unsheathing the sword"?

A Demand for Stronger Government

8. **Draw Conclusions** Which group led the movement toward a stronger government? What did they do and why? Use evidence from the text to support your answer.

9. **Analyze Interactions Among Events** In what way did the meetings at Mount Vernon in 1785, Annapolis in 1786, and Philadelphia in 1787 lead to the writing of the U.S. Constitution?

Lesson 2.4 Creating and Ratifying the Constitution

Key Terms

Framers

quorum

Virginia Plan

veto

New Jersey Plan

Connecticut Compromise

Three-Fifths Compromise

Commerce and Slave Trade Compromise

Federalists

Anti-Federalists

George Mason

Baron de Montesquieu

Jean Jacques Rousseau

William Blackstone

George Mason

Academic Vocabulary

envoy: a representative, especially in diplomatic affairs

apt: appropriate, correct, fit

amend: to change or modify

inauguration: a ceremonial introduction into office

unanimous: having the approval or consent of all

Lesson Objectives

1 **Identify** the Framers of the Constitution, the individuals, principals, and ideas that influenced them, how they organized the Constitutional Convention, and their contributions to the creation of the United States Constitution.

2 **Compare** and contrast the Virginia and the New Jersey plans for the new government.

3 **Examine** the convention's major debates and compromises.

4 **Identify** the opposing sides in the fight for ratification and describe the major arguments for and against the proposed Constitution.

The Framers Meet

1. **Interpret** The delegates who attended the Philadelphia Convention, and who came to be known as the Framers of the Constitution, included many outstanding individuals. Yet, Patrick Henry remarked that he "smelt a rat" and refused to attend the Convention. To what would you attribute his comment?

The Delegates Adopt Rules of Procedure

2. **Determine Central Ideas** What was the proposed reason for holding the Constitutional Convention? How did that idea change based on the resolution by Edmund Randolph from Virginia?

Two Plans of Government

3. **Draw Inferences** Read the second paragraph of "The Virginia Plan." In the plan, Virginia suggested that one way to determine representation would be based on financial contributions from each State. What does this fact tell you about Virginia's economy and population relative to the other colonies?

Interactive Reading Notepad • Lesson 2.4

4. **Compare and Contrast** Look at the chart in this text showing the features of the New Jersey Plan. In what way was the legislature created under this plan similar to the one that existed under the Articles of Confederation?

5. **Identify Central Ideas** Review the New Jersey Plan and the Virginia Plan. What is the basic conflict underlying the differences between the two plans? In what way would smaller or larger States be affected by each plan?

Debates and Compromises

6. **Support Ideas with Examples** Benjamin Franklin said that the convention spent much of its time "sawing boards to make them fit." Give three examples of decisions made during the Convention that support Franklin's comment.

7. **Integrate Information Read** the quotation below.

> ". . . when you assemble a number of men to have the advantage of their joint
> wisdom, you inevitably assemble with those men, all their prejudices, their
> passions, their errors of opinion, their local interests, and their selfish views."

—Benjamin Franklin

Now recall that the Articles of Confederation had created a structure that more closely resembled an alliance of independent states than a united nation. What relationship can you find between that fact and Franklin's words?

The Fight for Ratification

8. **Identify Key Steps in a Process** Describe the process by which the U. S. Constitution was adopted.

Interactive Reading Notepad • Lesson 2.4

9. **Assess an Argument** The quotation below is from *The Federalist*. It is titled "The Insufficiency of the Present Confederation to Preserve the Union." What main arguments are presented by Alexander Hamilton to defend the need for a new government? Give details from the excerpt to support your answer.

"We may indeed with propriety be said to have reached almost the last stage of national humiliation. There is scarcely anything that can wound the pride or degrade the character of an independent nation which we do not experience. . . . Do we owe debts to foreigners and to our own citizens contracted in a time of imminent peril for the preservation of our political existence? These remain without any proper or satisfactory provision for their discharge. Have we valuable territories and important posts in the possession of a foreign power which, by express stipulations, ought long since to have been surrendered? These are still retained, to the prejudice of our interests, not less than of our rights. Are we in a condition to resent or to repel the aggression? We have neither troops, nor treasury, nor government. . . . Is commerce of importance to national wealth? Ours is at the lowest point. . . ."

—*The Federalist* No. 15

10. **Integrate Information** What effect did Patrick Henry's statement— "I look on that paper as the most fatal plan that could possibly be conceived to enslave a free people"—have on Virginia's delegates? Why did Henry's opinion matter?

11. **Evaluate Explanations** The text says that "Had Jefferson fought as did other Anti-Federalists, Virginia might never have ratified the Constitution." Evaluate this statement. Why do you think Jefferson's support was so important to Virginia's ratification of the Constitution?

Lesson 3.1 An Overview of the Constitution

Key Terms

bicameral

Executive Article

inferior courts

popular sovereignty

limited government

constitutionalism

rule of law

separation of powers

checks and balances

veto

judicial review

unconstitutional

federalism

James Madison

Alexander Hamilton

Andrew Johnson

Donald Trump

Academic Vocabulary

political arena: the setting in which political activity occurs

provision: a clause that expresses a condition in a document or agreement

populous: with many people

predominates: holds controlling power or influence

couch: to express using a particular style

tribunal: a judicial body, a court

enshrined: set out with respect; honored

prohibition: a denial; a ban

vested: given to, conferred upon

override: to overturn, reverse, cancel

partisan: loyal to a particular political party

auxiliary: extra; supportive; supplemental

An Outline of the U.S. Constitution

1. **Determine Meaning of Words** Read the first paragraph under "Amendments." What does "cumbersome" mean? How would the U.S. Constitution be different if it included "cumbersome provisions," and how might this affect its longevity?

2. **Determine Central Ideas** The Constitution is "the supreme Law of the Land." How can this be seen by looking at the organization of the Constitution itself?

Article I

3. **Summarize** Use the graphic organizer to summarize historical, practical, and theoretical reasons why the Constitution establishes a bicameral legislature.

Reasons	Summary
Historical	
Practical	
Theoretical	

Article II

4. **Explain an Argument** The Framers debated two very different views of the presidency and how much power one person should have. Describe each argument. Which viewpoint is reflected in the Constitution?

Article III

5. **Vocabulary: Analyze Word Choices** Read the following quotation from Alexander Hamilton from *The Federalist* No. 78, in which Hamilton discusses the extent to which the judicial branch can influence the executive and legislative branches of government: "The judiciary . . . has no influence over either the sword or the purse; . . . It may truly be said to have neither FORCE nor WILL, but merely judgment." Why do you think Hamilton chose to use the words "sword" and "force" to refer to the executive branch and "purse" and "will" to refer to the legislative branch?

6. **Compare and Contrast** What is the key difference between the constitutional courts and the special courts?

Basic Principles

7. **Determine Central Ideas** As you read, list each of the three basic principles included in this text and describe the central idea of each in your own words.

8. **Draw Conclusions** In what way do citizens of today exercise popular sovereignty, and how do their actions provide an accurate reflection of the will of the citizens across the entire country?

9. **Integrate Information from Diverse Sources** Refer to the cartoon that illustrates separation of powers. Describe how the different characters each reflect the concept of separation of powers.

More Basic Principles

10. **Determine Central Ideas** As you read, list each of the three basic principles included in this text and describe each in your own words.

11. **Draw Conclusions** What do you suppose would happen if there was no system of checks and balances? Give an example of how this could affect the process of government.

12. **Use Visual Information** Refer to the Checks and Balances chart. How can the U.S. President directly affect the legislative and judicial branches of government? What can the legislature do if they do not agree with the President's selection of a judge?

Lesson 3.2 Amending the Constitution

Key Terms, Places, and People

amendment

ratification

formal amendment

Bill of Rights

executive agreement

treaty

electoral college

Cabinet

senatorial courtesy

Thomas Jefferson

Franklin D. Roosevelt

James Madison

George Washington

Lyndon Johnson

Academic Vocabulary

endure: to last a long time

provision: a feature, or something provided

permit: to allow for

advisory: serving as a recommendation

deprive: to keep away from someone

prohibition: a ban on something

skeletal: not detailed or fully developed

Lesson Objectives

1 **Describe** the constitutionally prescribed procedures by which the Constitution may be formally changed.

2 **Explain** how the amendment process illustrates federalism and popular sovereignty.

3 **Understand** the 27 amendments that have been added to the Constitution, and several that have been proposed but not ratified.

4 **Identify** how basic legislation has added to our understanding of the Constitution over time.

5 **Analyze** how interpretation of the Constitution has changed through the actions of the executive and judicial branches, and by party practices and customs.

Formal Amendment Process

1. **Identify Key Steps** For each formal method through which the Constitution can be amended, what are the steps of the process?

   I. Formal Amendment Process

   A. First Method

      1. _____

      2. _____

   B. Second Method

      3. _____

      4. _____

   C. Third Method

      5. _____

      6. _____

   D. Fourth Method

      7. _____

         _____

      8. _____

         _____

2. **Identify Supporting Details** Describe the method used to adopt 26 of the 27 amendments to the Constitution. Include evidence from the text to support your answer.

Federalism and Popular Sovereignty

3. **Cite Evidence** How does the formal amendment process illustrate the goals of the Framers? What requirements of the formal amendment process support your answer?

4. **Draw Inferences** Why do you think that a State legislature might want to call for an advisory vote by the people before it ratifies an amendment proposed by Congress?

Proposing an Amendment

5. **Identify Cause and Effect** Why do you think only 27 amendments have been added to the Constitution since its ratification, even though thousands have been proposed?

The 27 Amendments

6. **Summarize** Review the 27 amendments in the reading. In your own words, write the subject of each amendment to complete the chart.

Amendments	Subject	Amendments	Subject
1-10		19	
11		20	
12		21	
13		22	
14		23	
15		24	
16		25	
17		26	
18		27	

Change by Other Means

7. **Summarize** How has basic legislation added to our understanding of the Constitution over time?

8. **Cite Evidence** How has the interpretation of the Constitution changed through the actions of the executive and judicial branches and by party practices and customs? Use evidence from the text to support your answer.

Lesson 3.3 Federalism: Powers Divided

Key Terms

federalism

division of powers

delegated powers

expressed powers

implied powers

inherent powers

reserved powers

exclusive powers

concurrent powers

Supremacy Clause

John Marshall

Academic Vocabulary

enumerated: specified, listed, identified

reprieve: postponement or delay in the execution of a sentence

deport: to order that one be forced to leave a country

confiscate: to take or seize legally

illicit: illegal, unlawful, outlawed

pursuance: a carrying out of an execution of something

imperil: to endanger, put at risk, threaten

Lesson Objectives

1 **Define** Federalism and explain why the Framers adopted a federal system instead of a unitary system.

2 **Categorize** powers delegated to and denied to the National Government, and powers reserved for and denied to the States, and the difference between exclusive and concurrent powers.

3 **Summarize** the obligations that the Constitution, as "the supreme Law of the Land," places on the National Government with regard to the States.

The Founders Choose Federalism

1. **Compare and Contrast:** Compare the Framers' beliefs about local self-government to their attitude toward a strong central government.

2. **Identify Supporting Details:** Use examples to explain why the author describes the division of powers as "a very complex matter."

What is Federalism

3. **Summarize:** In your own words, provide a brief summary of federalism in the United States.

4. **Determine Meaning of Words** Define the expression "division of powers."

Three Types of Federal Powers

5. **Categorize:** Complete the chart with examples of the expressed, inherent, and implied powers of the National Government.

Expressed Powers	Inherent Powers	Implied Powers

6. **Analyze Word Choices:** The Necessary and Proper Clause says that Congress has the power

   "to make all Laws which shall be necessary and proper for carrying into Execution the foregoing Powers and all other Powers vested by this Constitution in the Government of the United States, or in any Department or Officer thereof."

   Why do you think the Framers used the words "necessary and proper" to describe the power of Congress to make laws?

Powers Denied to the Federal Government

7. **Summarize:** Briefly explain the concept of "the silence of the Constitution."

8. **Use Visual Information:** Look at the "Powers Denied to the Federal Government" chart. Choose one way in which power is denied to the Federal Government—Expressly Denied, Implicitly Denied, or Silently Denied—and use your own words to explain why the Federal Government should be denied those powers.

Powers of the Fifty States

9. **Paraphrase:** In your own words, describe the breadth of the powers reserved to the States.

The Exclusive and the Concurrent Powers

10. **Determine meaning of words:** Explain the meaning of the phrase "concurrent powers."

The Constitution Reigns Supreme

11. **Paraphrase:** In your own words, paraphrase the Constitution's Supremacy Clause.

12. **Cite evidence:** Cite specific examples to describe the important role the Supremacy Clause has played in American history.

Interactive Reading Notepad • Lesson 3.3

Lesson 3.4 The National Government and the States

Key Terms

enabling act

act of admission

grants-in-aid program

categorical grant

block grants

project grants

interstate compacts

Full Faith and Credit Clause

extradition

Privileges and Immunities Clause

William Howard Taft

Academic Vocabulary

integrity: the quality of being a single undivided whole

insurrection: a revolt against a government

forerunner: one that comes before, precedes

unwarranted: without legal authority

jurisdiction: the authority to interpret and apply the law

fugitive: one who flees

Lesson Objectives

1 **Explain** the process for admitting new States to the Union.

2 **Examine** the many and growing areas of cooperative federalism.

3 **Explain** why States make interstate compacts.

4 **Understand** the purpose of the Full Faith and Credit Clause, the Extradition Clause, and the Privileges and Immunities Clause.

The Nation's Obligations Under the Constitution

1. **Compare and contrast** Before the States agreed to give up their war-making powers, each demanded that an attack on any one of the States would be met as an attack on all of them. Compare the significance of this guarantee today to its significance at the time the Constitution was written.

Admitting New States

2. **Summarize** In your own words, summarize the process used to admit new States to the United States.

3. **Determine Meaning of Words** Define the term "enabling act."

States and Federal Government Sharing Resources

4. **Categorize** A State received one grant-in-aid for "health," one for "waste-water treatment," and one to conduct research on a treatment for uterine cancer. Categorize these three grants as project, categorical, or block grants. Then, write another example of each type of grant.

5. **Compare and Contrast** Compare the two perspectives on whether grants-in-aid support or undermine our Federal Government.

Interactive Reading Notepad • Lesson 3.4

Agreements Among States

6. **Determine Central Ideas** Why was it necessary to establish formal procedures for making agreements among or between States?

How the Law Crosses State Lines

7. **Paraphrase** In your own words, explain the meaning of the phrase "Full Faith and Credit."

Extradition

8. **Determine Meaning of Words** Define the word "extradition."

9. **Cite Evidence** Cite a specific example of a situation in which a request for extradition is likely to be contested.

Privileges and Immunities

10. **Identify Supporting Details** Explain the function and use of the Privileges and Immunities Clause.

11. **Draw Conclusions** Explain why a State college or university is able to hire out-of-state professors but charges out-of-state students a higher tuition rate.

Lesson 4.1 National Legislature Overview

Key Terms

delegates	convenes
trustees	adjourns
partisans	recess
politicos	prorogue
bills	special session
floor consideration	franking privilege
oversight function	Luther Patrick
term	Nancy Pelosi
session	Harry Truman

Academic Vocabulary

peculiar: unique, special, particular

appropriate: provide funds for a public purpose

agenda: list of things to be done

fringe benefits: compensation in addition to a base salary

offset: to balance, counteract, or compensate for

Lesson Objectives

1 **Explain** why the Constitution provides for the bicameral structure of Congress.

2 **Explain** the difference between a term and a session of Congress.

3 **Describe** a situation in which the President may convene or end a session of Congress.

4 **Identify** the personal and political backgrounds of members of Congress.

5 **Describe** the duties performed by those who serve in Congress.

6 **Describe** the compensation and privileges of members of Congress.

The Role of Congress in a Democracy

1. **Vocabulary: Determine Meaning** "The history of the present King of Britain," wrote Thomas Jefferson in the Declaration of Independence, "is a history of repeated injuries and usurpations, all having in direct object the establishment of an absolute tyranny over these States."

   What do you think the word "usurpations" means? What impact did this view of King George III's rule have on the form of government that emerged from the Declaration of Independence? Use evidence from the text to support your answer.

2. **Determine Author's Point of View** Use this concept web to take notes on the roles and voting options of members of Congress.

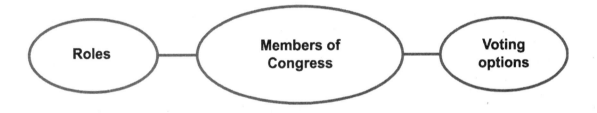

Congress—The Job

3. **Support a Point of View with Evidence** Use the text to write an opinion about the extent to which the composition of Congress *should* reflect that of the general population.

Terms and Sessions of Congress

4. **Use Visual Information** Refer to the text and the timeline. What is the relationship between terms and sessions of Congress? Why do you think the Framers established sessions of Congress?

5. **Draw Conclusions** In what ways are checks and balances applied to sessions of Congress?

Congressional Compensation

6. **Paraphrase** The late Senator Russell Long (D., Louisiana) characterized Congress's constitutional right to fix its own pay as "a power that no good man would want and no bad man should have." What do you think he meant?

7. **Draw Conclusions** How and why did the 27th Amendment modify the authority of Congress to set its own pay?

Lesson 4.2 The Two Houses

Key Terms

apportioned

reapportion

single-member district

at-large

gerrymandering

off-year elections

incumbent

continuous body

constituencies

James Madison

Woodrow Wilson

Robert C. Byrd

Academic Vocabulary

grossly: obviously

peculiar: unusual, odd

maneuvering: deal-making or strategy

susceptible: likely to be affected by, vulnerable

clout: power, influence

extralegal: informal, not covered by law

incumbency: the current holding of the office

concurrence: agreement

Lesson Objectives

1 **Explain** how House seats are distributed and describe the length of a term in the House.

2 **Explain** how House seats are reapportioned among the States after each census.

3 **Describe** a typical congressional election and congressional district.

4 **Analyze** the formal and informal qualifications for election to the House and the Senate.

5 **Compare** the size of the Senate to the size of the House of Representatives.

6 **Explain** how and why a senator's term differs from a representative's term.

The House

1. **Determine Author's Point of View** Thomas Jefferson, in a conversation with George Washington, expressed his opposition to a two-chambered legislature, while pouring his coffee into a saucer to cool it. Pointing out the similarity to the purpose of the two-chambered legislature, George Washington replied, "…we pour legislation into the senatorial saucer to cool it."

   What do you think George Washington meant? Consider this quotation, and the information in the text, as you answer this question: How does the distribution of Senate seats among the States illustrate the principle of federalism?

Reapportionment of Congress

2. **Integrate Information from Diverse Sources** Study the map of reapportionment in 2010. What overall trends in population movement are seen? What is the significance of census results for each State's congressional districts?

Interactive Reading Notepad • Lesson 4.2

House Elections

3. **Draw Conclusions** In the 1994 mid-term election, the Democratic party lost 52 seats in the House, down to 206 seats total, and 8 seats in the Senate, down to 45 seats total. What effect do you think this had on the Democratic President's legislative agenda?

Qualifications for Office in the House

4. **Support a Point of View with Evidence** Of the different informal qualifications for membership in the House mentioned in the text, which do you think are most significant in obtaining a seat?

5. **Infer** Read the text about the events detailing the political career of Victor L. Berger of Wisconsin. What can you infer about the democratic process from this series of events?

Interactive Reading Notepad • Lesson 4.2

The Senate: Size, Election, and Terms

6. **Analyze Charts** Study the graph on the growth of the membership of the House and Senate. What factors influenced the growth of the Senate and the House? What could account for the time periods when the greatest number of seats were added to the Senate and the House?

7. **Vocabulary: Analyze Word Choices** "It is harder for a poor man to enter the United States Senate than for a rich man to enter Heaven." In what way does this aphorism from the late nineteenth century express the popular movement that resulted in ratification of the 17th Amendment?

Qualifications for Office in the Senate

8. **Compare and Contrast** Compare and contrast the constitutional, as well as customary, requirements for the House and Senate. What do you think the Framers intended in differentiating the requirements? Do you agree?

Lesson 4.3 The Expressed Powers

Key Terms

expressed powers

implied powers

inherent powers

commerce power

tax

public debt

deficit financing

bankruptcy

legal tender

copyright

patent

territory

eminent domain

naturalization

Hudson River

John Marshall

District of Columbia

Bill Clinton

Boston

Philadelphia

Benjamin Franklin

Lyndon B. Johnson

Richard Nixon

Academic Vocabulary

sweeping: wide-ranging

impotent: powerless

creditor: person to whom money is owed

Lesson Objectives

1 **Describe** the three types of powers delegated to Congress.

2 **Understand** the expressed powers of Congress.

3 **Identify** the key sources of the foreign relations powers of Congress.

4 **Describe** the power-sharing arrangement between Congress and the President on the issues of war and national defense.

5 **List** other key domestic powers exercised by Congress.

Types of Congressional Powers

1. **Identify Supporting Details** Under "Types of Congressional Powers," what details support the idea that government in the United States is limited government and that the American system of government is federal in form?

2. **Draw Conclusions** Read the third paragraph of "The Expressed Powers." Select one of the questions listed regarding the scope of the Commerce Clause, and record it in the table, below. As you read the rest of the text for this lesson, record notes about the question, and then write and explain a conclusion for the following question: Do you consider this an example of the Commerce Clause?

The Scope of the Commerce Clause

Does "commerce" include:	Notes	Conclusion

The Commerce Power

3. **Draw Inferences** Read the section on *Gibbons* v. *Ogden*, 1824. Consider the possible effects if the Supreme Court had ruled in Ogden's favor, instead of siding with Gibbons. List examples from the text that might have resulted in different outcomes if this had been the case.

4. **Draw Inferences** Read "Limits on the Commerce Power." Why do you think the Framers placed each of the first three limits on the use of the commerce power?

The Money Powers

5. **Identify Supporting Details** As you read "The Money Powers," use this table to record information about each of the money powers that Congress is granted.

The Money Powers

Power	What May Congress Do?	What Limits are Placed on Congress?	Examples
Taxing			
Borrowing			
Bankruptcy			
Currency			

Interactive Reading Notepad • Lesson 4.3

Other Domestic Powers

6. **Compare and Contrast** How are copyrights and patents similar? How are they different? Cite examples from the text to support your answer.

7. **Draw Conclusions** Some believe that the U.S. Postal Service should be abolished because its functions could be performed more efficiently by private, for-profit mail companies. Do you agree or disagree? Explain.

8. **Use Visual Information** Look at the image of "The Atomic Clock." Discuss the significance of this example of congressional powers of weights and measures. What might be some of the consequences if Congress did not have the power to establish one central, uniform system of timekeeping?

Congress and Foreign Policy

9. **Draw Inferences** Read the first paragraph of "Congress and Foreign Policy." How might the foreign policy of the United States be different if the Constitution had not forbidden the individual States from making treaties or alliances with foreign powers?

The War Powers

10. **Cite Evidence** The constitutionality of the War Powers Resolution remains in dispute. Explain this resolution. Do you think it is constitutional? Why or why not?

Interactive Reading Notepad • Lesson 4.3

Lesson 4.4 The Implied and Nonlegislative Powers

Key Terms

Necessary and Proper Clause	censure	Antonin Scalia
strict constructionist	subpoena	Donald Trump
liberal constructionist	successor	Neil Gorsuch
consensus	Thomas Jefferson	Andrew Johnson
appropriate	Alexander Hamilton	Abraham Lincoln
impeach	Barack Obama	Richard Nixon
acquit	George W. Bush	John Quincy Adams
perjury	Samuel Alito	

Academic Vocabulary

ardent: committed, passionate

enmeshed: entangled, caught up in

conciliatory: producing agreement

concur: agree

Lesson Objectives

1 **Explain** how the Necessary and Proper Clause gives Congress flexibility in lawmaking.

2 **Compare** the strict construction and liberal construction positions on the scope of congressional power.

3 **Describe** the ways in which the implied powers have been applied.

4 **Describe** the investigatory and executive powers of Congress

5 **Describe** the power of Congress to impeach.

6 **Describe** the role of Congress in amending the Constitution and its electoral duties.

The Necessary and Proper Clause

1. **Draw Conclusions** What is the Necessary and Proper Clause? Explain how this clause gives Congress flexibility in lawmaking.

2. **Assess an Argument** Congress has used the Necessary and Proper Clause to establish a minimum wage. Use evidence from the text to describe the positions a strict constructionist and a liberal constructionist would take in response to this action.

The Doctrine in Practice

3. **Draw Conclusions** Why is the Commerce Clause, written in 1787, still adequate to meet the needs of the twenty-first century? Cite an example from the text to support your opinion.

4. **Draw Conclusions** What might have happened if the National Government could only legislate based on what is specifically in the Constitution? Provide examples to support your opinion.

The Power to Investigate

5. **Use Visual Information** Look at the image of Senator Joseph McCarthy leading a congressional hearing that appears at the opening of this lesson and consider the reasons that Congress holds hearings. Which of these do you think could be used to justify the congressional investigations that Senator McCarthy conducted? What about more recent investigations?

Executive Powers

6. **Integrate Information From Diverse Sources** Use the text and the table "Examples of Senate Rejections of Cabinet Nominees." Explain what is unusual about the data provided about John Tyler.

Impeachment

7. **Identify Supporting Details** As you read "Impeachment," use this table to record information about the three presidential impeachment cases.

The Three Presidential Impeachment Cases

President	Year	Offenses	House Actions	Senate Actions	Result

Other Powers

8. **Draw Inferences** Explain why Congress has the ultimate authority to override the President on many matters or propose amendments to the Constitution.

Lesson 4.5 Congress at Work: Organization and Committees

Key Terms

Speaker of the House
president of the Senate
president *pro tempore*
party caucus
floor leaders
majority leader
minority leader
whips

committee chairperson
seniority rule
standing committee
subcommittee
select committee
joint committee
conference committee
Joe Biden

Academic Vocabulary

preside: to act in the role of chairperson

quorum: a minimum number of members required to do business

judicious: reasonable

jurisdiction: the range of matters under the committee's control

miscreants: criminals, wrongdoers

Lesson Objectives

1 **Describe** how and when Congress convenes.

2 **Compare** the roles of the presiding officers in the Senate and the House.

3 **Identify** the duties of the party officers in each house.

4 **Describe** how committee chairmen are chosen and explain their role in the legislative process.

5 **Explain** how standing committees function.

6 **Describe** the role of select committees.

7 **Compare** the functions of joint and conference committees.

Congress Convenes

1. **Draw Inferences** During the opening day of congress, the House of Representatives adopts the rules that will govern its proceedings through the new term. Why do you think in 2009 the rules were amended to repeal a limit on the number of terms that any member can chair any House committee?

2. **Vocabulary: Determine Meaning** Read the quotation from Article II, Section 3 of the United States Constitution. Explain the meaning of this article in your own words.

3. **Draw Inferences** Why do think the President has almost always given the State of the Union Address in person, since 1913?

The Presiding Officers

4. **Draw Inferences** Why do you think that neither the Constitution nor the rules of the House require the Speaker of the House to be chosen from among the members of the House or from the majority party?

5. **Paraphrase** The Speaker of the House is expected to preside in a fair and judicious manner and is expected to aid the fortunes of the majority party and its legislative goals. In your own words, describe what this means.

Party Officers

6. **Draw Inferences** Why do you think party officers are chosen during the party's caucus, before the Opening Day, in both the House and the Senate?

7. **Draw Inferences** After reading about the responsibilities of floor leaders, why do you think Senator Howard Baker (R., Tennessee) often likened his job to that of "herding cats"?

8. **Draw Conclusions** Why is it important that the party whips learn how many members will be present for a vote and how members are voting on a particular topic?

Committee Chairs

9. **Assess an Argument** Do you agree with the seniority rule? Why or why not?

Standing Committees

10. **Draw Inferences** What did Representative Clem Miller (D., California) mean when he described Congress as, "a collection of committees that come together in a chamber periodically to approve of one another's actions"?

11. Draw Conclusions Why is the House Rules Committee often described as the "traffic cop" in the House of Representatives?

Select Committees

12. Explain an Argument Do you agree with the congressional power to investigate given to select committees? Why or why not?

Joint and Conference Committees

13. Summarize Briefly describe the roles of the joint and conference committees. Why is it important that these committees exist in our legislative branch?

Lesson 4.6 Congress at Work: Making Law

Key Terms

bill

joint resolution

concurrent resolution

resolution

rider

pigeonholed

discharge petition

quorum

engrossed

filibuster

cloture

veto

pocket veto

omnibus measure

Huey Long

Strom Thurmond

Academic Vocabulary

voluminous: massive; lengthy

sieve: a sifting device, gatekeeper

latitude: leeway, range of action

Lesson Objectives

1 **Identify** the first steps in the introduction of a bill to the House.

2 **Describe** what happens to a bill once it is referred to a committee.

3 **Explain** what happens to a bill on the House floor.

4 **Describe** how a bill is introduced in the Senate.

5 **Compare** the Senate's rules for debate with those in the House.

6 **Describe** the role of conference committees in the legislative process.

7 **Evaluate** the actions the President can take after both houses have passed a bill

---

The First Steps

1. **Sequence Events** You are a member of Congress who has agreed to sponsor legislation to publicly recognize the bravery of soldiers who served in Iraq. Name two of the steps that you will take to move this legislation forward.

2. **Check Understanding** Each session of Congress considers many different types of legislation. Choose how to classify each of the issues below by using the following list: public bill, private bill, joint resolution, concurrent resolution, and simple resolution.

Description	Legislation type
An amendment to the Constitution prohibiting citizens from carrying assault weapons	
A statement of support for the government of Haiti's efforts to rebuild after the earthquake	
A proposal to require universities to pay taxes	
A requirement that a roll call be taken for all votes in the House	
A proposal for an interstate highway to take a rancher's land by eminent domain	
A declaration of war against Germany	

3. **Generate Explanations** Why is the *Congressional Record* "not quite a word-for-word account" of the proceedings in the House or Senate? Why might a member of Congress want to make changes to the *Record* before it is published?

4. **Analyze Information** Congress is notoriously slow at acting on most legislation in each session. Consider the first steps in making a law. Which step would you eliminate to speed up the process? Why?

5. **Infer** A spending bill in 2011 attracted a rider that would repeal energy efficiency standards for light bulbs and another to reinstate travel restrictions from the United States to Cuba. Why were these riders tied to a spending bill? Do you think Congress should change its rules to prevent riders? Why or why not?

The Bill in Committee

6. **Apply Concepts** How do committees and subcommittees help keep the legislative process running smoothly? Use evidence from the text to support your answer.

7. **Apply Concepts** If you are the sponsor of a bill, what can you do to keep it from being pigeonholed?

8. **Generate Explanations** Why are committees sometimes called "little legislatures"? Consider the responsibilities of a committee chairperson in your answer.

Scheduling Floor Debate

9. **Make Decisions** You are part of a special committee to streamline procedures in the House of Representatives. Your first task is to reorganize the calendar for scheduling floor debate. Describe one major change you would make and explain how it would streamline the legislative process.

10. **Evaluate Arguments** The Rules Committee "plays a critical role in the legislative process." Do you think this committee has too much power? Why or why not?

The Bill on the House Floor

11. **Draw Conclusions** How does the Committee of the Whole help the House of Representatives manage debates?

12. **Analyze Information** Why are quorum calls and record votes important in House voting procedures?

The Bill on the Senate Floor

13. **Analyze Information** Do unanimous consent agreements ensure that every bill gets a thorough hearing in the Senate? Why or why not?

14. **Check Understanding** How does a filibuster protect the minority party?

House-Senate Conference Committees

15. Explain Why is a bill that is approved by one chamber of Congress likely to be approved by the other without change?

16. Cite Evidence Why is a conference committee considered a "most strategic step" in the passage of a bill?

The President Acts on a Bill

17. Hypothesize If the legislature best represents the voice of the people, why does the Constitution require the President to act on bills and resolutions passed by Congress?

18. Draw Conclusions What happens when a President takes no action on a bill instead of signing or vetoing it? Why might a President want to do this?

Unorthodox Lawmaking and Emergency Legislation

19. Generate Explanations How does an omnibus measure help streamline the traditional legislative process?

20. Draw Inferences In a vote on a national emergency, why are members of Congress held more accountable for an unpopular decision than the President, who is also elected by citizens?

Lesson 5.1 The Presidency: An Overview

Key Terms

chief of state

chief executive

domestic affairs

foreign affairs

chief administrator

chief diplomat

chief legislator

commander in chief

chief economist

chief of party

chief citizen

presidential succession

impeachment

Presidential Succession Act
 of 1947

president *pro tempore*

William Howard Taft

Harry Truman

Franklin D. Roosevelt

Lyndon B. Johnson

Richard Nixon

John F. Kennedy

Theodore Roosevelt

Bill Clinton

Barack Obama

Donald Trump

Ronald Reagan

Herbert Hoover

Dwight Eisenhower

Alexander Hamilton

George Washington

George H.W. Bush

William Henry Harrison

Woodrow Wilson

George W. Bush

Academic Vocabulary

sprawling: spreading out over a large area

concert: with all in agreement, together as one

champion: to fight for, defend, or promote

agonizing: painful, distressing

sordid: shameful

arbitrary: high-handed, unreasonable

Lesson Objectives

1 **Describe** the President's many roles.

2 **Understand** the formal qualifications necessary to become President.

3 **Explain** how the number of terms for which a President may serve has changed over time.

The President's Many Roles

1. **Summarize** As you read "The President's Many Roles," use this graphic organizer to keep track of the presidential roles and the responsibilities each entails. Use your completed outline to analyze the ways in which the expectations for the additional presidential roles differ from those that are specified by the Constitution.

I. **The President's Roles – Constitutional**

  A. **Chief of state**

      1. _____

      2. _____

  B. 1. _____

      2. _____

  C. 1. _____

      2. _____

  D. 1. _____

      2. _____

  E. 1. _____

      2. _____

  F. 1. _____

      2. _____

II. **The President's Roles – Additional**

  A. 1. _____

      2. _____

  B. 1. _____

      2. _____

  C. 1. _____

      2. _____

2. **Cite Evidence** As you've read, in many countries, the chief of state reigns but does not rule. Cite evidence from your reading on the President's many roles to support the statement that the President of the United States both reigns and rules.

Qualifications for the Presidency

3. **Draw Conclusions** What are the formal qualifications for the office of the President, and why do you think the Framers specified these requirements?

4. **Draw Inferences** In an upcoming campaign, two candidates want to run for President. Their qualifications are as follows:

Candidate A

- 47 years old
- college graduate
- lived in the U.S. through college; currently living and working in Italy
- born in the United States

Interactive Reading Notepad • Lesson 5.1

Candidate B

- 54 years old
- attended college, but didn't graduate
- born in France to American citizens
- moved to U.S. at age 20; has lived here since that time

Which candidate might have his/her candidacy questioned based on which constitutional provision?

The Presidential Term of Office

5. **Compare and Contrast** In what way did George Washington and Franklin D. Roosevelt differ in their approaches to presidential term limits? How were those beliefs reflected in their presidencies? With which of these two men would President Reagan have agreed?

6. **Draw Conclusions** Consider the following event: The Vice President succeeds to the presidency when the President dies 18 months into his first term of office. Can he then run for President when that term is over? If he runs and wins, can he seek more than one term as President? What constitutional provision addresses this issue?

Presidential Succession and Disability

7. **Identify Key Steps in a Process** In each scenario below, identify the next step that would occur to address the situation and the law that would apply to each circumstance.

   A. The President dies of natural causes.

   B. Both the President and Vice President are killed in a plane crash.

   C. The President dies and the Vice President is sworn in as President, but needs emergency surgery before a new Vice President is chosen. She will be unable to make decisions for about 12 hours.

8. **Summarize** In what way did the Presidential Succession Act of 1947 and the 25th Amendment clarify the Constitution's handling of presidential vacancies?

9. **Cite Evidence** What is the "disability gap," and why was it important that it be filled? Include at least one example from the reading to support your answer.

10. **Analyze Sequence** Recall what you have learned about the 25th Amendment. Consider the following events and then analyze the sequence of steps that would be taken to address the situation. Rearrange them to show the correct order that would be followed.

The President is hurt in a serious accident. He is unable to speak. After recovering, the President believes that he is ready to resume his duties, but the Vice President and Cabinet members disagree.

Steps taken to address the situation:

1. Vice President and a majority of the Cabinet challenge the President on his declaration of health.

2. Vice President becomes Acting President.

3. Congress has 21 days in which to make a decision.

4. Vice President and majority of Cabinet inform Congress in writing that the President is incapacitated.

5. President resumes the powers and duties of the office.

6. President informs Congress by "written declaration" that no disability exists.

Lesson 5.2 The Vice President and the First Lady

Key Terms

balance the ticket
First Lady

Academic Vocabulary

ideological: having to do with the beliefs or ideas of a person or group
proliferation: a rapid increase in number or amount
buttress: to strengthen

Lesson Objectives

1 **Analyze** the functions of the executive branch of government in terms of the formal duties the Constitution assigns to the Vice President.

2 **Describe** how the role of the Vice President has changed over time.

3 **Explain** the part played by First Ladies throughout the nation's history.

The Structure and Function of the Vice Presidency

1. Use this chart to organize information from this text.

	Vice President
How does this person come into office?	
Where is this person in the line of presidential succession?	
What are some responsibilities of this office?	

2. **Vocabulary: Use Context Clues** Read the second paragraph of "Early Vice Presidents." What do you think the word *superfluous* means? Why do you think Benjamin Franklin thought the Vice President was *superfluous*? Use evidence from the text to support your answer.

3. **Draw Inferences** Read the quotation from Thomas Marshall in the section "Early Vice Presidents." How might a recent Vice President, such as Dick Cheney or Joe Biden, respond to this quotation?

4. **Identify Cause and Effect** Look at the image in the text that shows the testing of an atomic bomb in 1945. In what way did this event affect the role of the Vice President?

The First Lady

5. **Summarize** Select two First Ladies who were discussed in the text and explain how each approached her role as First Lady. Discuss the impact each made on the role. Use evidence from the text to support your answer.

6. **Determine Author's Point of View** "This was I and yet not I, this was the wife of the President of the United States and she took precedence over me; my personal likes and dislikes must be subordinated to the consideration of those things which were required of her."

    —First Lady Grace Coolidge, wife of President Calvin Coolidge

    Reflect on these words from First Lady Grace Coolidge. What do they say about the role of the First Lady?

Lesson 5.3 The President's Domestic Powers

Key Terms

executive orders

ordinance power

executive privilege

reprieve

pardon

clemency

commutation

amnesty

veto

pocket veto

line-item veto

Andrew Jackson

Abraham Lincoln

Andrew Johnson

Gerald Ford

James Madison

James Monroe

Ulysses S. Grant

Academic Vocabulary

imperil: to put in danger

seizure: taking by force

discretion: the freedom to act according to one's judgment

depose: to remove from a position of power

candor: the quality of being open and honest in speaking

malfeasance: wrong or illegal conduct by a public official

absolute: final, not subject to appeal

Lesson Objectives

1 **List** the reasons for the growth of presidential power and explain how the system of checks and balances limits that growth.

2 **Understand** the constitutional powers of the President, including the President's power to execute the law and issue executive orders.

3 **Explain** how certain provisions of the U.S. Constitution provide for checks and balances among the three branches of the government.

4 **Examine** the powers of executive privilege and clemency.

5 **Explain** the legislative powers and how they are an important part of the system of checks and balances.

The Growth of Presidential Power

1. **Identify Supporting Details** Use the graphic organizer to identify the reasons for the growth of presidential power.

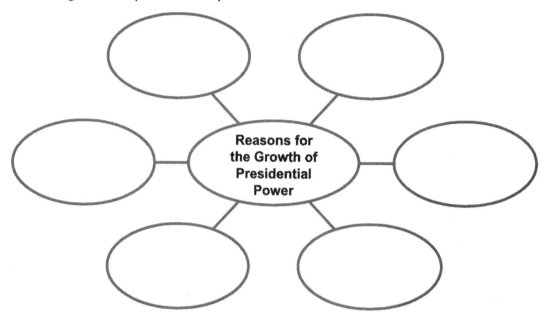

2. **Vocabulary: Determine Meaning of Words** Read the fourth paragraph of the text "Limits to Power." What do you think the word *contentious* in this paragraph means? Why do you think the description of Congress as *contentious* is an accurate one in this case? Use evidence from the text to support your answer.

The Power to Execute the Law

3. **Draw Inferences** Immigration laws require that all immigrants seeking permanent admission to the United States must be able to "read and understand some dialect or language." The U.S. Citizenship and Immigration Services decides how well immigrants must be able to "read and understand." How is this situation an example of the separation of powers between the legislative and executive branches?

4. **Paraphrase** In your own words, explain what Thomas Jefferson meant when he wrote "The execution of the laws is more important than the making of them." How does this idea reflect on the power of the presidency?

Executive Orders and Executive Privilege

5. **Cite Evidence** What evidence can you find in the text to support this statement: The job of administering federal laws is extremely challenging.

6. **Draw Inferences** How is the President's ordinance power established by the Constitution?

7. **Integrate Information From Diverse Sources** Read the text on executive orders. Then look at the photograph of the federal worker. What different information about executive orders can you draw from both sources?

8. **Determine Central Ideas** Does the idea of executive privilege safeguard or disrupt the separation of powers between the executive and the legislative branches?

The Powers of Appointment and Removal

9. **Draw Inferences** Consider this statement: The unwritten rule of senatorial courtesy contradicts the principle of separation of powers. Do you agree or disagree? Explain why.

10. **Use Visual Information** Use the chart "Who Gets the Job?" to explain the importance of Senate committees and Senate debates as part of the appointment process.

The Powers of Clemency

11. **Categorize** Make a brief list of the President's judicial powers and explain each item on your list.

12. **Assess an Argument** The judicial powers of the President help maintain the system of checks and balances in the government. Do you agree with this statement? Why or why not?

The Power to Recommend Legislation

13. **Identify Cause and Effect** How does the role of chief legislator help the President contribute to the creation of new federal laws?

The Power of the Veto

14. **Determine Central Ideas** How might the line-item veto increase the legislative powers of the President?

15. **Use Visual Information** What does the chart "The Power of the Veto" tell you about the use of the veto power by various Presidents and the with which Congress they are working? Use evidence from the chart to support your answer.

16. **Draw Conclusions** How do signing statements expand presidential power?

Lesson 5.4 The President's Foreign Affairs Powers

Key Terms

treaty

John Tyler

William McKinley

executive agreement

recognition

persona non grata

Academic Vocabulary

supersede: to take the place of something previously in use

rebuke: an expression of sharp disapproval

invariably: always, without exception

Lesson Objectives

1 **Explain** how treaties are negotiated by the President, approved by the Senate, and ratified by the President under the system of checks and balances.

2 **Explain** why and how executive agreements are made.

3 **Summarize** how the power of recognition is used by the President.

4 **Describe** the President's constitutional powers as commander in chief.

The President's Diplomatic Powers

1. **Summarize** In negotiations with another sovereign state, the President sometimes makes a treaty, but other times signs an executive agreement. Use the graphic organizer to list the major features of each.

Treaty	Executive Agreement

2. **Identify Key Steps** When the Senate does not approve a treaty, what measures can the President take to maneuver around this type of check and balance of power? Use an example from the reading in your answer.

3. **Infer** In 1933, President Franklin D. Roosevelt formally recognized the Soviet Union. During the Cold War of the 1950s and 1960s, military threats between the United States and the Soviet Union escalated, but the United States did not withdraw its recognition of that country. Why would a President want to continue recognizing a country when it has expressed hostility towards the United States?

Interactive Reading Notepad • Lesson 5.3

4. **Identify Cause and Effect** Why is it of interest to the entire world if the President asks for the recall of another nation's ambassador?

5. **Determine Central Ideas** In the treaty-making process, how do the President and Congress act as checks and balances on each other? Can Congress ever repeal a treaty? Can the President use a treaty to repeal a law? When do the courts get involved in treaties?

Commander in Chief

6. **Use Visual Information** Look at the photograph of President Abraham Lincoln visiting United States troops during the Civil War. What authority did President Lincoln have to talk to soldiers in the field? How might these visits have helped the war effort?

7. **Analyze Interactions** The United States has not declared war against another country since 1942, yet it has been involved in several military actions since then. Name one of these actions. Did Congress and the President work together to support this undeclared war? Explain.

8. **Analyze Interactions** The War Powers Resolution of 1973 gives the President the power to order troops into combat when the United States is directly attacked. Why, then, did Congress need to pass a special resolution allowing the President to use force against the nations involved in the terror attacks of September 11, 2001?

Lesson 6.1 The Federal Bureaucracy

Key Terms

bureaucracy   staff agency

bureaucrat   line agency

administration   James Madison

Academic Vocabulary

inclination: a tendency, preference, attitude

uniformity: sameness, regularity

standardize: to set up according to a rule or model

distinction: a difference between two or more things

Lesson Objectives

1 **Define** a bureaucracy.

2 **Identify** the major elements of the federal bureaucracy.

3 **Explain** how groups within the federal bureaucracy are named.

4 **Describe** the difference between a staff agency and a line agency.

What Is a Bureaucracy?

1. **Determine Author's Point of View** Read the following quotation from Walter Bagehot from 1867:

   "A bureaucracy is sure to think that its duty is to augment [increase] official power, official business, or official members, rather than to leave free the energies of mankind; it overdoes the quantity of government, as well as impairs its quality."

   What is the author's opinion of bureaucracy? How does it compare with the opinion expressed by James Madison (quoted in Text 1)?

2. **Draw Conclusions** How does bureaucracy increase the effectiveness of the Federal Government? At the same time, how does bureaucracy limit the Federal Government's effectiveness?

3. **Analyze Cartoons** Read again Walter Bagehot's 1867 quotation:

"A bureaucracy is sure to think that its duty is to augment [increase] official power, official business, or official members, rather than to leave free the energies of mankind; it overdoes the quantity of government, as well as impairs its quality."

Then refer to the "What Is a Bureaucracy?" text, and locate the political cartoon. How does the cartoon illustrate Bagehot's point regarding overdoing the quantity of government and impairing its quality?

Executive Branch Bureaucracy

4. **Categorize** Refer to the "Executive Branch Bureaucracy" text. Show the hierarchy of organization in the executive branch of the Federal Government by completing the graphic organizer.

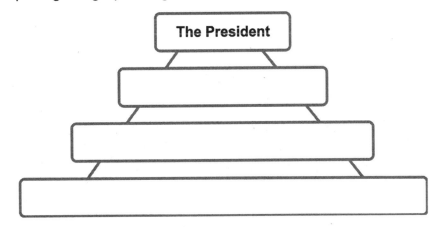

The President

Interactive Reading Notepad • Lesson 6.1

5. **Identify Supporting Details** What does the Constitution say about the administration of the executive branch?

How Units Are Named

6. **Identify Supporting Details** In what way are names for government agencies common, but not standardized?

7. **Draw Conclusions** Why do you think so much inconsistency exists in the names of the various government agencies?

Staff and Line Agencies

8. **Analyze Interactions** As you read "Staff and Line Agencies," make notes on how staff agencies and line agencies are different entities that work together.

9. **Categorize** The Office of Management and Budget assists the President in preparing the budget, and NASA is responsible for pioneering the future in space exploration. Categorize each as a staff or line agency, and explain why.

Lesson 6.2 The EOP and the Executive Departments

Key Terms

Executive Office of the President

federal budget

fiscal year

domestic affairs

executive department

civilian

secretary

attorney general

George Washington

Abraham Lincoln

Academic Vocabulary

inner circle: those most influential, closest to the center of power

clout: influence, power

realm: a particular field or area

multidimensional: having several parts

practical: learned through practice or action

cog: part, element of an organization

eclipse: overshadow, surpass, outshine

Lesson Objectives

1 **Analyze** the structure and functions of the executive branch of government.

2 **Describe** the Executive Office of the President.

3 **Explain** the duties of the White House, the National Security Council, and the Office of Management and Budget.

4 **Identify** other agencies that make up the Executive Office of the President.

5 **Describe** the role of the Cabinet and executive departments in the executive branch.

Structure of the Executive Office of the President

1. **Summarize** Complete the chart to show the functions of some of the agencies and advisors that are part of the Executive Office of the President.

Advisor or Agency	Function
White House Chief of Staff	
National Security Council	
Office of Management and Budget	
Office of National Drug Control Policy	
Council of Economic Advisers	
Domestic Policy Council	
Council on Environmental Quality	

The Executive Departments

2. **Draw Inferences** Why do you think it is important that the President select executive department heads?

3. **Analyze Interactions** In what ways can the chief officers and staff of the executive departments support the President's policy agenda?

4. **Cite Evidence** Each department is made up of subunits and those subunits are composed of sections. What aspect of this structure do you think allows these departments to direct the work of staff who are located in many places across the nation? Cite evidence in the text to support your answer.

The Cabinet and Its Functions

5. **Identify Cause and Effect** The role and importance of the Cabinet has changed over time. How has it changed, and how have various Presidents contributed to those changes? Use evidence from the text to support your answer.

6. **Draw Inferences** Read the quotation by William Howard Taft. What do you think the author means by the statement that "William Howard Taft put the Cabinet in its proper light?" Use evidence from the text to support your answer.

Lesson 6.3 The Independent Agencies

Key Terms

independent agencies

independent executive
 agencies

civil service

patronage

spoils system

draft

independent regulatory
 commissions

government corporations

Andrew Jackson

James Garfield

Chester Arthur

Theodore Roosevelt

Jimmy Carter

Academic Vocabulary

limelight: the focus of attention

catchall: all-inclusive, covering a wide range of possibilities

induction: the process of installing somebody into military service

stagger: to arrange something so that it does not occur at the same time

---

Lesson Objectives

1 **Explain** why Congress created the independent agencies.

2 **Identify** the characteristics of independent executive agencies.

3 **Describe** the history, purpose, and effect on private enterprise of selected independent executive agencies and regulatory commissions, including NASA and the EPA.

4 **Explain** the structure and function of government corporations.

The Purpose of Independent Agencies

1. **Summarize** As you read "The Purpose of Independent Agencies," provide four reasons why Congress located the independent agencies outside of Cabinet departments. What do you think would happen if the independent agencies were located within Cabinet departments?

2. **Vocabulary: Use Context Clues** Read the third paragraph under "Reasons for Independent Agencies." What does *partisan* mean in this sentence and why is a lack of partisan politics important to independent agencies? Use evidence from the text to support your answer.

Independent Executive Agencies

3. **Compare and Contrast** Use the Venn diagram to compare and contrast the three types of independent agencies as you read the remainder of the texts: "Independent Executive Agencies," "Independent Regulatory Commissions," and "Government Corporations."

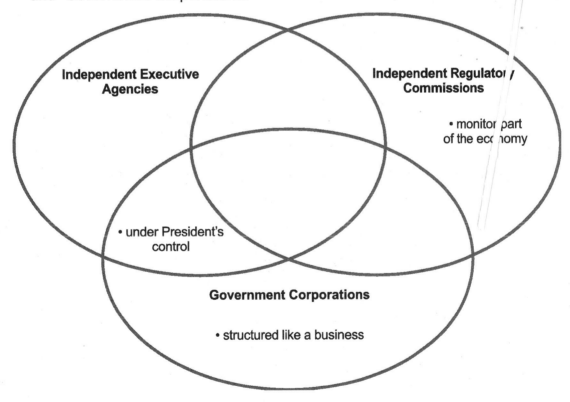

Independent Executive Agencies

Independent Regulatory Commissions

• monitor part of the economy

• under President's control

Government Corporations

• structured like a business

Interactive Reading Notepad • Lesson 6.3

4. **Cite Evidence** Read the following excerpt from Upton Sinclair's *The Jungle*:

"There would be meat stored in great piles in rooms; and the water from leaky roofs would drip over it, and thousands of rats would race about on it. . . . These rats were nuisances, and the packers would put poisoned bread out for them; they would die, and then rats, bread, and meat would go into the hoppers together . . . with fresh meat, and sent out to the public's breakfast."

Could these conditions exist in today's meat-packing plants? Explain using evidence from the text.

5. **Identify Cause and Effect** How has the process of selecting federal workers changed throughout our history, and what caused this change?

6. **Use Visual Information** Look at the photos in the interactive illustration on NASA. Describe these and other civilian advancements made possible by NASA's military work.

Independent Regulatory Commissions

7. **Explain an Argument** Many argue that regulatory commissions have been influenced by the special interests they are expected to regulate. Do you agree? Give an example to support your thinking.

8. **Determine Central Ideas** The Nuclear Regulatory Commission licenses and regulates the use of nuclear energy to protect public health, safety, and the environment. It also sets rules and standards for nuclear reactors, facilities, and waste materials. These are important issues to U.S. citizens. Why is it most effective for this to be handled by a regulatory commission instead of by Congress?

Government Corporations

9. **Compare and Contrast** How are government corporations similar to private corporations? How are they different?

10. **Determine Central Ideas** What role does the President play in the structure and/or functioning of government corporations?

Lesson 6.4 Foreign Policy Overview

Key Terms

foreign policy	cold war	Dwight Eisenhower
domestic affairs	containment	John F. Kennedy
foreign affairs	détente	Lyndon Johnson
isolationism	Isthmus of Panama	Ronald Reagan
collective security	Pearl Harbor	
deterrence	Harry Truman	

Academic Vocabulary

sanction: penalty imposed for hostile acts

doctrine: a rule or principle that forms the basis of a policy or belief

plague: to cause continuing trouble, distress

quell: to put down

scourge: something that causes great trouble or suffering

posture: to adopt a pose, usually intended to deceive

counter: to oppose, contradict

armistice: an agreement to stop fighting for a time, a cease-fire

divisiveness: disagreement, hostility, split

Lesson Objectives

1 **Explain** the major responsibilities of the Federal Government for foreign policy.

2 **Summarize** U.S. foreign policy during the first 150 years of its history, including its adherence to isolationism.

3 **Show** how World War II finally ended America's traditional policy of isolationism, giving way to internationalism and the principles of collective security and deterrence.

4 **Analyze** how today's U.S. foreign policy affects selected places and regions, as well as the significance to the United States of the location and key natural resources of selected global places or regions.

What is Foreign Policy?

1. **Use Visual Information** Read the text and look at the images in this lesson, including the lesson opener. In what ways can foreign policy influence domestic policy in the United States?

Beginnings Through World War I

2. **Draw Conclusions** In what ways did the policy of isolationism and the creation of the Monroe Doctrine shape American foreign policy in the late 1700s and early 1800s?

3. **Paraphrasing** Read the section titled "The Monroe Doctrine," then paraphrase that content to explain what led to the issuing of the Monroe Doctrine in 1823.

4. **Compare and Contrast** Why might the Roosevelt Corollary be seen as a natural extension of the Monroe Doctrine? In what way was it different from that policy?

Interactive Reading Notepad • Lesson 6.4

5. **Summarize** Use information from throughout this lesson to complete the timeline and show how our relations with China have changed over time.

U.S.–China Relations

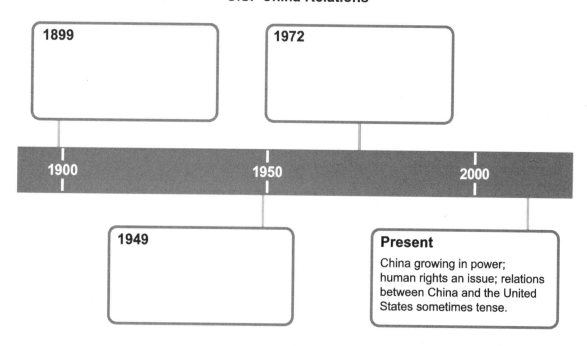

World War II to the End of the Cold War

6. **Identify Cause and Effect** What long-term effect did the overall shift in foreign policy away from isolationism during World War II have on America's position in the world?

7. **Summarize** Describe the different foreign policies that the United States has practiced over time with regard to the Soviet Union.

8. **Vocabulary: Determine Meaning** Read the following excerpt from the text.

"The cold war was a period of more than 40 years during which relations between the two superpowers were at least tense and, more often than not, distinctly hostile. It was, for the most part, not a "hot war" of military action, but rather a time of threats, posturing, and military buildup."

What does the word *posturing* mean as it is used in this sentence?

Today's Foreign Policy Challenges

9. **Distinguish Among Fact, Opinion, and Reasoned Judgment** Is it critical for the United States to continue its heavy involvement in world affairs? Write your opinion about this question. Then write one fact to support it. Finally, change your statement of opinion to one of reasoned judgment.

10. **Identify Supporting Details** What details in the reading "Today's Foreign Policy Challenges" support the idea that foreign policy today is complex and requires a delicate balance of interests?

Lesson 6.5 Diplomacy

Key Terms

right of legation

ambassador

diplomatic immunity

passport

visa

foreign aid

regional security alliance

NATO

United Nations

Security Council

Thomas Jefferson

Madeleine Albright

Colin Powell

Condoleezza Rice

Hillary Rodham Clinton

Rex Tillerson

Ayatollah Khomeini

George C. Marshall

Balkans

Slobodan Milosevic

Franklin D. Roosevelt

Winston Churchill

Academic Vocabulary

accredit: to send a diplomatic representative with proper credentials

destabilize: to make something unstable, undermine, upset

organ: a unit of organization that performs a specific function

abstain: to choose not to participate

jurisdiction: authority of a court to hear and decide a dispute

Lesson Objectives

Lesson Objectives

1 **Describe** the functions, components, and organization of the State Department.

2 **Examine** how the U.S. government uses economic resources in foreign policy, including foreign aid.

3 **Examine** the history, structure, and work of the United Nations and its relationship with the United States

America's Representatives to the World

1. **Draw Inferences** Why do you think the author describes the State Department as "the President's right arm in foreign affairs?"

2. **Vocabulary: Determine Meaning of Words** The text states that Some chief executives have chosen to delegate a large share of the responsibility for matters of foreign policy to the secretary of state." What is the meaning of the word *delegate* in this context?

3. **Use Visual Information** Read the information about passports and visas in the text and in the "Travel Documents" chart. Then answer these questions:
   - If you were traveling to China, would you need a passport, a visa, or both?
   - Which type of document limits a visit to a specific length of time?

American Foreign Aid

4. **Determine Central Ideas** How did America's first foreign aid programs impact the balance of world power? Cite evidence from the text to support your answer.

5. **Assess an Argument** Consider the following argument in favor of continued economic aid to other nations and then assess validity: Foreign economic aid to other countries is a good investment for the United States. It comprises only 1 percent of the entire federal budget, some $20 billion dollars, and yet returns untold amounts in increased sales of American goods and services.

NATO

6. **Analyze Sequence** How has NATO's composition and mission evolved over time?

7. **Draw Inferences** Why do you think NATO became involved with the ouster of Libya's Qaddafi and ongoing anti-terrorist activities in the Middle East, the Mediterranean, and East Africa?

The United Nations

8. **Summarize** Use the chart below to summarize the purpose and work of the UN General Assembly and Security Council. If you find any other information about these governing bodies as you read the text, add it to the row labeled "Other."

	UN General Assembly	UN Security Council
Membership		
Purpose		
Meetings		
Other		

9. **Identify Supporting Details** What details under "The United Nations" help to explain why the United States took a leading role in the UN's creation?

The UN's Work

10. **Paraphrase** Use your own words to describe the overall mission of the UN.

11. **Determine Author's Point of View** What details help to explain why the author describes America's relationship with the UN as "complex"?

Lesson 6.6 National Security

Key Terms
espionage
terrorism

Academic Vocabulary
spearhead: to lead a military force; to take the lead in
campaign: a series of military actions taken toward a specific goal
shroud: to hide from view
ideological: having to do with the ideas or beliefs of a group

---

Lesson Objectives

1 **Summarize** the functions, components, and organization of the Defense Department and its military departments.

2 **Explain** how the Director of National Intelligence and the Department of Homeland Security contribute to national security.

The Department of Defense

1. **Draw Inferences** How might World War II have contributed to the decision to create a single Department of Defense in 1947?

2. **Cite Evidence** Cite evidence supporting the statement that "The Framers . . . recognized the dangers inherent in military power and its abuse."

Branches of the Military

3. **Identify Cause and Effect** Why has the number of active duty soldiers in the army declined?

4. **Compare and Contrast** Complete the chart to show how the three branches of the military differ. Include information related to the age, area of operations, and mission of each branch.

Three Branches of the Military		
Army	Navy	Air Force

The Director of National Intelligence

5. **Summarize** Describe the work conducted by the Office of the Director of National Intelligence (DNI).

6. **Draw Inferences** Why do you think the budget of the DNI is disguised within the federal budget?

The Department of Homeland Security

7. **Determine Meaning of Words** Define and provide examples of terrorism.

8. **Analyze Interactions** Explain how the Department of Homeland Security operates at all levels of government, including federal, State, and local.

9. **Use Visual Information** Look at the interactive gallery outlining a day at the Department of Homeland Security. Of the four areas listed in the chart, which do you think poses the greatest challenge to the department? Why?

Lesson 7.1 The National Judiciary

Key Terms

inferior courts

jurisdiction

concurrent jurisdiction

plaintiff

defendant

original jurisdiction

appellate jurisdiction

judicial activism

precedent

judicial activism

Sandra Day O'Connor

Ruth Bader Ginsburg

Sonia Sotomayor

Elena Kagan

Thurgood Marshall

Clarence Thomas

Antonin Scalia

Neil Gorsuch

District of Columbia

Academic Vocabulary

tribunal: a judicial body, a court

infringement: violation

jurist: an expert in the law, especially a judge or legal scholar

premise: reason that forms the basis of an argument or conclusion

---

Lesson Objectives

1 **Explain** why the Constitution created a national judiciary, and analyze its structure and functions.

2 **Identify** the criteria that determine whether a case is within the jurisdiction of a federal court, and compare the types of jurisdiction.

3 **Outline** the process for appointing federal judges, and list their terms of office.

4 **Understand** the impact of judicial philosophy, and analyze issues raised by judicial activism and judicial restraint.

5 **Examine** the roles of court officers.

The Courts and Democracy

1. **Draw Conclusions** Why do you think that most of the Bill of Rights addresses the rights of the accused?

Creation of a National Judiciary

2. **Analyze Interactions** During the years 1781–1789 when the Articles of Confederation were in still force, there was no federal court system. How were the laws of the United States interpreted and applied at that time?

3. **Cite Evidence** In *The Federalist* No. 22, Alexander Hamilton refers to a "circumstance which crowns the defects of the Confederation." What circumstance is he referring to? How can you tell that he feels strongly about this matter?

Jurisdiction in the Federal Court System

4. **Summarize** Under what circumstances do federal courts have jurisdiction in a case?

5. **Integrate Information from Diverse Sources** Read the second paragraph of "Jurisdiction in the Federal Court System." Then look at the image of the capsized ship. What do the text and the image each tell you concerning federal court jurisdiction?

6. **Evaluate Explanations** Why did the Framers give the federal courts jurisdiction in all admiralty and maritime cases?

Types of Jurisdiction

7. **Identify Cause and Effect** As you read "Original and Appellate Jurisdiction," use this graphic organizer to record the three possible effects of a court with original jurisdiction sending a decision on to an appellate court.

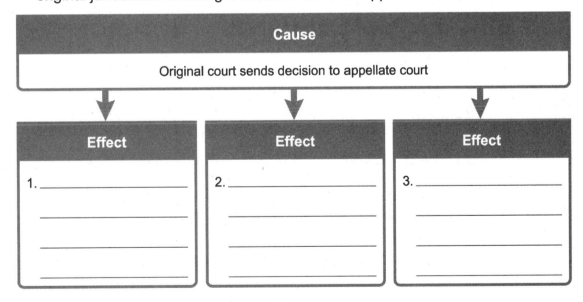

Cause
Original court sends decision to appellate court

Effect	Effect	Effect
1. _____	2. _____	3. _____

Interactive Reading Notepad • Lesson 7.1

8. **Analyze Interactions** What does it mean when it is said that the federal courts exercise both exclusive and concurrent jurisdiction?

9. **Determine Meaning of Words** Read the first paragraph of "Exclusive Jurisdiction." What do you think the word *infringement* means? Why do you think an infringement of a patent or copyright must be tried in a federal court?

Federal Judges and Court Officers

10. **Draw Inferences** What role does judicial philosophy play in the selection of judges?

11. **Identify Supporting Details** What requirements for federal judges are detailed in the Constitution?

12. **Compare and Contrast** How do the length of terms for constitutional court judges and special court judges compare?

13. **Summarize** What role do United States magistrates play in the federal court system?

Lesson 7.2 The Supreme Court

Key Terms

judicial review
writ of certiorari
certificate
brief
majority opinion
concurring opinion

dissenting opinion
James Madison
John Marshall
Thomas Jefferson
William Marbury

Academic Vocabulary

aftermath: result or consequence

implement: to carry out, to put into effect

underpin: to support or strengthen

Lesson Objectives

1 **Define** the concept of judicial review, and identify the roles played by Thomas Jefferson, James Madison, and John Marshall in the case in which the Court first asserted its power of judicial review.

2 **Outline** the types of jurisdiction that apply to the Supreme Court.

3 **Explain** how cases reach the Supreme Court.

4 **Summarize** the way the Supreme Court operates.

What is Judicial Review?

1. **Determine Meaning of Words** Read the section titled "*Marbury* v. *Madison*." What does the word *jurisdiction* mean? What does it mean if a court does not have *jurisdiction* over a particular case?

2. **Analyze** Consider the interactions between the Supreme Court, William Marbury, Thomas Jefferson, and James Madison in *Marbury* v. *Madison*. How did the Court give itself more power by denying that it had the jurisdiction to hear the case?

3. **Draw Inferences** Does the Court's decision in *Marbury* v. *Madison* to exercise judicial review make U.S. democracy more stable, or less so?

Jurisdiction of the Supreme Court

4. **Paraphrase** Notice the word *exclusive* in the third paragraph of this section. Explain what it means for the Supreme Court to have original and *exclusive* jurisdiction over certain cases.

5. **Categorize** Give an example of each of the Court's two types of jurisdiction.

Appealing to the Supreme Court

6. **Identify Key Steps in a Process** Make a list of all the steps that must take place if a case is to be heard on appeal before the Supreme Court.

7. **Draw Conclusions** How do justices decide whether or not to accept a case on appeal?

8. **Identify Cause and Effect** What factors do you think affect the number of cases that the Court is able to hear in a term?

Hearing a Supreme Court Case

9. **Draw Inferences** What groups of people do you think read and follow Supreme Court decisions most closely? Why?

10. **Identify Cause and Effect** Why do justices write concurring and dissenting opinions? What effect do concurring and dissenting opinions have on future cases?

Interactive Reading Notepad • Lesson 7.2

Lesson 7.3 The Inferior Courts and the Special Courts

Key Terms

criminal case

civil case

docket

record

courts-martial

civilian tribunal

redress

Guantanamo Bay, Cuba

Academic Vocabulary

litigant: party to a case, either plaintiff or defendant

indict: accuse, bring charges against

valid: legitimate, well-grounded

Lesson Objectives

1 **Describe** the structure and jurisdiction of the federal district courts, the federal courts of appeals, and other constitutional courts.

2 **Contrast** the jurisdiction of the Court of Appeals for the Armed Forces and the Court of Appeals for Veterans Claims.

3 **Explain** how a citizen may sue the United States government in the Court of Federal Claims.

4 **Examine** the roles of the territorial courts and those of the District of Columbia courts.

5 **Explain** what types of cases are brought to the Tax Court.

The Structure and Role of the Federal District Courts

1. **Summarize** Describe the different roles played by Congress in the federal district courts.

2. **Draw Conclusions** The daily routines of one federal district court judge might vary greatly from the routines of another. Explain why these court officials around the country can have a common job title but very different experiences on the job.

The Structure and Role of the Federal Courts of Appeals

3. **Identify Supporting Details** How can a case reach a federal court of appeals without having gone to trial in any court previously?

4. **Analyze Sequence** Read the information about a case that is given in the flow chart below. Then explain the next step in the case.

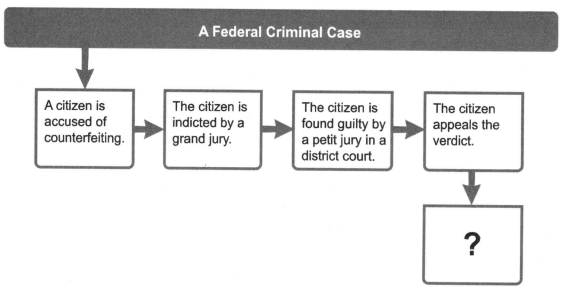

A Federal Criminal Case

A citizen is accused of counterfeiting. → The citizen is indicted by a grand jury. → The citizen is found guilty by a petit jury in a district court. → The citizen appeals the verdict. → **?**

5. **Compare and Contrast** Think about how cases are heard in the federal district courts vs. the federal appeals courts. If a judge describes herself as "an outgoing person who enjoys witnessing human interaction," in which of the two types of courts would she be more comfortable, and why?

The Court of International Trade

6. **Draw Inferences** Why are jury trials in the Court of International Trade often held in port cities?

Military Justice: Special Courts and Commissions

7. **Analyze Interactions** Explain how the three branches of government are or are not involved in the formation of a legitimate military commission.

8. **Categorize** Why is the Court of Appeals for Veterans Claims neither a court of first instance nor a court of final instance?

Other Special Courts

9. **Identify Cause and Effect** Describe a circumstance in which the findings of the Court of Federal Claims would be meaningless.

10. **Compare and Contrast** What does the United States Tax Court have in common with courts-martial? With the Court of International Trade?

Lesson 8.1 The Unalienable Rights

Key Terms

Bill of Rights

civil liberties

civil rights

alien

Due Process Clause

process of incorporation

Robert H. Jackson

Oliver Wendell Holmes, Jr.

Pearl Harbor

James G. Blaine

Academic Vocabulary

regime: a government

orthodox: standard, recognized, accepted

arbitrary: random

vulgarity: an offensive or indecent act or expression

stringent: strict, rigid, narrow

Lesson Objectives

1 **Explain** how Americans' commitment to freedom led to the creation of the Bill of Rights.

2 **Understand** that the obligation of citizenship requires that personal desires and interests be subordinated to the public good.

3 **Describe** efforts to extend some of the protections of the Bill of Rights to the States and analyze the impact of that process on the scope of fundamental rights and federalism.

4 **Describe** how the 9th Amendment helps protect individual rights.

A Commitment to Individual Rights

1. **Identify Supporting Details** As you read the lesson "The Unalienable Rights," use this concept web to identify the parts of the Constitution that protect individual rights.

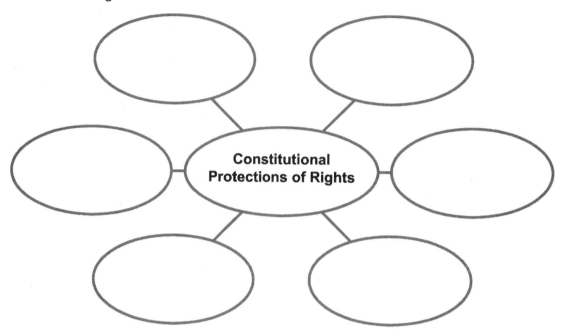

2. **Identify Key Steps in a Process** Describe the events that led to the adoption of the Bill of Rights. Explain how these events reflected a commitment to personal freedom.

3. **Compare and Contrast** Compare and contrast *civil liberties* and *civil rights*. What distinctions can be made between the two terms?

Limited Government

4. **Paraphrase** Read Justice Robert H. Jackson's opinion from *West Virginia Board of Education* v. *Barnette*, 1943. Paraphrase his statement.

"If there is any fixed star in our constitutional constellation, it is that no official, high or petty, can prescribe what shall be orthodox in politics, nationalism, religion, or any other matters of opinion or force citizens to confess by word or act their faith therein."

—West Virginia Board of Education *v.* Barnette, *1943*

5. **Explain an Argument** How does the following quotation by Justice Oliver Wendell Holmes from *Schenck* v. *United States* illustrate the concept that "rights are relative, not absolute"?

"The most stringent protection of free speech would not protect a man in falsely shouting fire in a theatre and causing a panic."

—Schenck *v.* United States, *1919*

6. **Use Visual Information** Look at the image showing a Japanese American internment camp during World War II. How does this image illustrate the issues that were involved in the forced evacuation of American citizens of Japanese descent? Discuss the reasons for and against this practice. Explain how our government responded years later.

The 14th Amendment, Fundamental Rights, and Federalism

7. **Use Visual Information** Look at the "Incorporation of Rights" chart. Summarize which amendments from the Bill of Rights have been incorporated into the 14th Amendment's Due Process Clause.

8. **Summarize** Write a brief that applies to the 1925 *Gitlow* v. *New York* Supreme Court case. Include the following elements: statement of facts, statement of main issue, arguments, conclusion, and a summary of the case's significance.

9. **Compare and Contrast** As you read the text "Federalism and Fundamental Rights," use this graphic organizer to record your thoughts on the following questions: What are some of the characteristics of the 9th Amendment? What are some of the characteristics of the 14th Amendment? How are these two amendments similar?

The 9th Amendment and the 14th Amendment

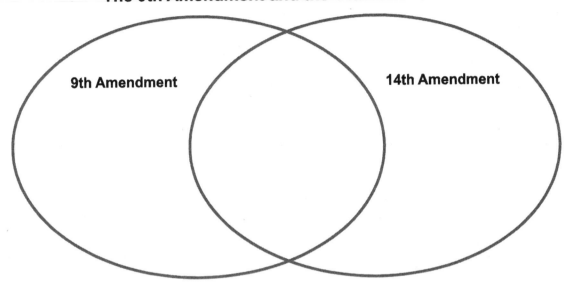

9th Amendment

14th Amendment

Lesson 8.2 Freedom of Religion

Key Terms

Establishment Clause

Free Exercise Clause

parochial

Alexis de Tocqueville

Academic Vocabulary

sect: a religious group

secular: nonreligious

sectarian: religious

endorsement: approval or backing of

Lesson Objectives

1 **Examine** the reasons the Founding Fathers protected religious freedom and guaranteed its free exercise.

2 **Understand** the meaning of the phrase "separation of church and state."

3 **Analyze** Supreme Court interpretations of religious rights guaranteed by the Constitution in selected cases relating to education.

4 **Summarize** Establishment Clause rulings in other areas, such as seasonal religious displays, and public displays of the Ten Commandments.

5 **Evaluate** Supreme Court decisions that have affected a particular religious group, in particular those related to the Free Exercise Clause.

Religious Liberty

1. **Determine Central Ideas** As you read the lesson "Freedom of Religion," use this graphic organizer to record information about Supreme Court cases that protect freedom of religion. Select and list the four cases that you think are the most significant, and include a statement explaining why you think each case is significant.

Freedom of Religion

Case	Ruling	Significance

2. **Draw Inferences** Consider what Alexis de Tocqueville wrote in *Democracy in America*. Explain what you think he meant when he wrote that it was not until he went into the churches that he "came to understand the genius and the power of this country."

Interactive Reading Notepad • Lesson 8.2

Religion and Education

3. **Categorize** Categorize each of the following as "constitutional" or "unconstitutional" based on the criteria established in *Lemon* v. *Kurtzman*.

   1. a law that provides for reimbursements to private schools to cover their costs for teachers' salaries, textbooks, and other teaching materials in nonreligious courses

   2. the use of public funds to pay for field trips for parochial school students

   3. a law that provides for church-related schools to be reimbursed for the costs of administering State standardized tests

   4. the use of public funds to pay any part of the salaries of parochial school teachers who teach secular courses

   5. the use of public funds to provide an interpreter for a deaf student in a Catholic high school

   6. a law that creates a school district to benefit handicapped Jewish children

4. **Summarize** Consider released time programs and summarize Supreme Court rulings on this issue.

Other Establishment Clause Cases

5. **Compare and Contrast** The text discusses two public displays of the Ten Commandments. Which was allowed to remain partly because it is part of a larger display of historical and cultural markers? Which was ordered to be removed because it amounted to an endorsement of religion by government?

The Free Exercise Clause

6. **Identify Supporting Details** As you read the text "The Free Exercise Clause," use this graphic organizer to record information about how the Supreme Court has ruled on cases involving the Free Exercise Clause. Record limits the Court has placed on the free exercise of religion, and examples of instances in which the Court has upheld the free exercise of religion.

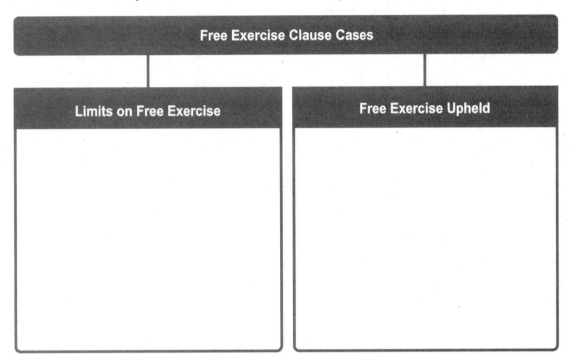

Free Exercise Clause Cases	
Limits on Free Exercise	**Free Exercise Upheld**

Lesson 8.3 Freedom of Speech and Press

Key Terms

libel

slander

sedition

seditious speech

symbolic speech

picketing

prior restraint

injunction

shield law

John Roberts

Oliver Wendell Holmes, Jr.

Academic Vocabulary

run afoul of: to come into conflict with, become entangled with

insubordination: rebellion or disobedience

scurrilous: insulting or scandalous

utterance: remark, statement

pedagogical: educational, academic, instructional

commodity: article that can be bought or sold

dissemination: distribution

Lesson Objectives

1 **Analyze** the purpose and importance of the 1st Amendment rights of free speech and press.

2 **Analyze** Supreme Court interpretations of rights guaranteed by the constitution in *Schenck* v. *U.S.* and other rulings related to seditious and obscene speech.

3 **Define** symbolic and commercial speech and describe the limits on their exercise, including Supreme Court interpretations of rights guaranteed by the Constitution in *Texas* v. *Johnson.*

4 **Examine** the issues of prior restraint and press confidentiality, and describe the limits the Court has placed on the media.

The Right of Free Expression

1. **Identify Central Issues** In what ways are the rights of free speech and press limited?

2. **Draw Conclusions** What is libel? What is slander? Why is truth an adequate defense against a claim of either one?

3. **Draw Conclusions** A citizen has written a letter to the editor of the local newspaper, accusing a local restaurant owner of adding fake charges to customers' bills. Can the restaurant owner sue? Why or why not?

Seditious Speech

4. **Make Generalizations** What was significant about the case *Schenck* v. *U.S.*?

5. **Compare and Contrast** Compare and contrast the interpretation of the Smith Act of 1940 in the cases of *Dennis* v. *U.S.* and *Yates* v. *U.S.*

The 1st Amendment and Symbolic Speech

6. **Summarize** The Supreme Court has made several rulings on acts of symbolic speech. Use the graphic organizer to identify at least six cases and how the Court ruled in each.

Supreme Court Rulings on Symbolic Speech

Supreme Court Case	Ruling

7. **Analyze Interactions** In the case *Tinker* v. *Des Moines*, the Court found that school officials had violated students' right to free expression. Furthermore, the Court emphasized that neither students nor teachers can be expected to "shed their constitutional rights to freedom of speech or expression at the schoolhouse gate." Yet, the Court has also endorsed the "comprehensive authority of school officials to prescribe and control conduct in the schools." How can these two positions coexist?

Prior Restraint on Expression

8. **Apply Concepts** A Nebraska State trial judge forbade all press coverage of a murder trial. In *Nebraska Press Association* v. *Stuart*, 1976, the Supreme Court held that the order was unconstitutional. What was the likely basis for this decision?

The Media in a Free Society

9. **Draw Inferences** Why do you think the Supreme Court has given broader 1st Amendment freedoms to cable television than to traditional network television?

10. **Determine Central Ideas** In what way do shield laws limit government regulation of the media?

11. **Evaluate Arguments** The Court has established a three-part test to define obscenity, including applying "local community standards" in determining whether materials are offensive. How might the "local community" element of the test be affected when considering materials sent over the Internet?

Lesson 8.4 Freedom of Assembly and Petition

Key Terms

assemble

petition

civil disobedience

content neutral

right of association

Academic Vocabulary

inherent: natural to or basic

Lesson Objectives

1 **Analyze** the importance of the 1st Amendment rights of petition and assembly.

2 **Analyze** Supreme Court interpretations of rights guaranteed by the Constitution, including limits on the time, place, and manner of assembly.

3 **Compare and contrast** the freedom-of-assembly issues that arise on public versus private property.

4 **Explore** how the Supreme Court has interpreted freedom of association.

Constitutional Provisions

1. **Determine Central Ideas** Why is the right to assemble peaceably important to a democratic society?

2. **Cite Evidence** At what point does a constitutionally protected right to assemble become a case of civil disobedience? Cite evidence from the text to support your answer.

Time, Place, and Manner Rules

3. **Analyze Information** Complete the graphic organizer as you read this section. Then use it to answer these questions: On what basis can the government regulate assemblies? How do these parameters protect citizens' constitutional rights?

Case	Issue	Ruling
Grayned v. *City of Rockford*, 1972		
Cox v. *Louisiana*, 1965		
Coates v. *Cincinnati*, 1971		
Forsyth County v. *Nationalist Movement*, 1992		

Assemblies on Public and Private Property

4. **Compare and Contrast** Compare and contrast the Court's rulings regarding demonstrations in the cases of *Gregory* v. *Chicago* and *Lloyd Corporation* v. *Tanner*, 1972. What was the basis for the Court's decisions in each case?

5. **Apply Concepts** Suppose you were part of a group demonstrating in front of city hall and you were arrested because the group had not given the city advance notice of the demonstration. Would your arrest be upheld by the Supreme Court? Explain your answer.

Freedom of Association

6. **Determine Central Ideas** How does the constitutional right of association extend the constitutional right of assembly?

7. **Evaluate Explanations** The Supreme Court has upheld the right of association as an "inseparable aspect" of the Constitution's guarantees of free expression. Moreover, they have held that there is no *absolute* right of association. Explain the differences between these two aspects of the right of association.

Lesson 8.5 Due Process of Law

Key Terms

due process
procedural due process
substantive due process

police power
search warrant
eminent domain

Academic Vocabulary

compulsory: forced, obligatory

Lesson Objectives

1 **Explain** the importance of due process rights to the protection of individual rights and in limiting the powers of government.

2 **Define** police power and understand its relationship to the subordination of personal desires and interests to the public good.

Understanding Due Process

1. **Determine Central Ideas** The 5th Amendment declares that the Federal Government cannot deprive any person of "life, liberty, or property, without due process of law." The 14th Amendment places that same restriction on all State and local governments as well. Why is it important that the 14th Amendment places that same restriction on State and local governments?

2. **Draw Conclusions** Explain the logic behind the Supreme Court's unanimous decision in *Rochin* v. *California*, 1952, that the deputies in the case had violated the 14th Amendment's guarantee of procedural due process. What can you conclude from the fact that the decision was unanimous?

3. **Explain an Argument** Explain why the Supreme Court held that the Oregon compulsory school-attendance law, requiring all persons between the ages of eight and sixteen to attend public schools, violated the 14th Amendment's guarantee of substantive due process.

4. **Compare and Contrast** Use the Venn diagram to show how procedural due process and substantive due process are alike and different. Include a definition and an illustrative court case for each type of due process.

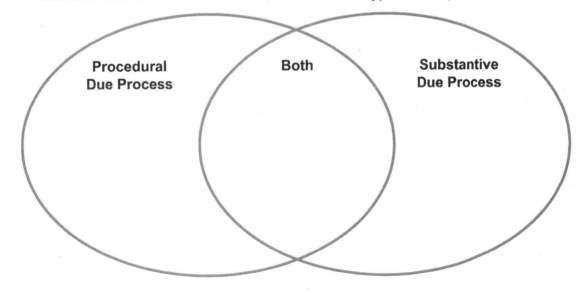

Procedural Due Process | Both | Substantive Due Process

Individual Rights and the Public Good

5. **Integrate Information from Diverse Sources** Courts must often strike a balance between protecting public health, safety, morals, and general welfare and protecting individual freedoms. State and federal courts often decide in favor of the police power, however. Think of an example to demonstrate this fact, other than those found in the text.

6. **Assess an Argument** Eminent domain is the right of the government to take private property for public use; however, the government must provide the owners with just compensation. Look at the photograph of a home destroyed by Hurricane Sandy. The government is planning to tear this home down and replace it with a sand dune for future protection against such storms. Do you agree with eminent domain in this case, and in general? Why or why not?

Interactive Reading Notepad • Lesson 8.5

Lesson 8.6 Freedom and Security of the Person

Key Terms

involuntary servitude
discrimination
writs of assistance

probable cause
exclusionary rule

Academic Vocabulary

encroachment: intrusion, invasion
tainted: spoiled, tarnished, flawed
traitorous: disloyal, guilty of betrayal

Lesson Objectives

1 **Evaluate** how Supreme Court decisions regarding slavery and involuntary servitude have affected a particular racial group.

2 **Analyze** the importance of the 2nd Amendment's protection of the right to keep and bear arms.

3 **Evaluate** constitutional provisions for limiting the role of government, including those designed to guarantee the security of home and person.

4 **Understand** the Supreme Court's ongoing refinement of the exclusionary rule, including its ruling in *Mapp* v. *Ohio*.

5 **Describe** the right to privacy and its origins in constitutional law and Supreme Court interpretations or rights guaranteed by the Constitution in selected cases, including *Roe* v. *Wade*.

Slavery and Involuntary Servitude

1. **Draw Inferences** The 13th Amendment forbids slavery and involuntary servitude anywhere within the United States. However, drafting young men into the military and forcing prisoners to work are legal. Why is this?

2. **Draw Conclusions** The Supreme Court ruled in favor of Jones in the case *Jones* v. *Mayer*, 1968, declaring that Congress has the power to abolish "the badges and incidents of slavery." How was Mayer's refusal to sell Jones a home considered a badge and incident of slavery?

Right to Keep and Bear Arms

3. **Paraphrase** The 2nd Amendment reads: "A well regulated Militia, being necessary to the security of a free state, the right of the people to keep and bear Arms, shall not be infringed." What does this amendment mean to you in your own words? What has the Supreme Court said it means?

Security of Home and Person

4. **Cause and Effect** Why has the 3rd Amendment had little importance since 1791?

5. **Categorize** As you read "Security of Home and Person," place a check mark in the column labeled "Allowable" if evidence obtained through each method described can be used in court. If evidence obtained in this manner cannot be used in court, place a check mark in the column labeled "Not Allowable."

Security of Home and Person

Action	Allowable	Not Allowable
Evidence obtained in a home or on a person without a warrant		
Evidence obtained "in plain view"		
Evidence obtained via informational roadblocks		
Evidence obtained in a moving vehicle when there is probable cause to believe the vehicle is being used for illegal activities		

The Exclusionary Rule

6. **Summarize** As you read "The Exclusionary Rule," add at least four actions to the chart in question 5 above. Mark whether the actions are "Allowable" or "Not Allowable" based on the amendments or court rulings discussed in the text.

Security of Home and Person

Action	Allowable	Not Allowable

7. **Explain an Argument** Provide one argument for and one argument against the exclusionary rule.

8. **Use Visual Information** Look at the infographic entitled "Exceptions to the Exclusionary Rule." How well do each of the four exceptions protect an individual's 4th Amendment right against unlawful searches and seizures? Rank each exception in order from *most protective* to *least protective*. Explain your rankings. Use information from the text to support your rankings.

The Right of Privacy

9. **Draw Conclusions** What does the text mean when it says, "As the composition of the Court has changed… so has the Court's position on abortion."

10. **Identify** According to the Supreme Court's ruling in *Roe* v. *Wade*, at what point can the State legally prohibit abortion?

Interactive Reading Notepad

Lesson 8.7 Rights of the Accused

Key Terms

writ of habeas corpus

bill of attainder

ex post facto law

grand jury

indictment

presentment

information

double jeopardy

bench trial

Miranda rule

bail

preventive detention

capital punishment

treason

Abraham Lincoln

Roger B. Taney

Academic Vocabulary

waive: to give up or forgo

subpoena: to legally summon, order to appear

legitimate: valid, sound, lawful

capriciously: unpredictably; erratically, without reason

exonerate: to declare innocent, absolve, free of blame

Lesson Objectives

1 **Understand** the role of limited government in the protection of individual rights, including protections relating to the writ of habeas corpus, bills of attainder, and ex post facto laws.

2 **Outline** how the right to a grand jury and the guarantee against double jeopardy help safeguard the rights of the accused.

3 **Describe** issues that arise from guarantees of speedy and public trials.

4 **Identify** the freedoms and rights guaranteed by the Bill of Rights, including the right to a fair trial by jury.

5 **Examine** Supreme Court interpretations in selected cases of the right to an adequate defense and the guarantee against self-incrimination, including *Gideon* v. *Wainwright* and *Miranda* v. *Arizona*.

Article I Protections

1. **Determine Central Ideas** As you read this lesson, consider how the Constitution protects the rights of the accused. Complete the chart to show how the following features of the justice system protect the rights of the accused at different stages.

The Right of the Accused

Right	How the Right Protects the Accused
reading of Miranda rights	
writ of habeus corpus	
grand jury	
jury trial	
prohibition against cruel or unusual punishment	

2. **Draw Conclusions** Why was a Supreme Court ruling on the imprisonment of foreign-born prisoners in Guantanamo Bay necessary?

3. **Determine Central Ideas** How do bills of attainder and ex post facto laws reflect the principle of separation of powers?

Interactive Reading Notepad • Lesson 8.7

4. **Analyze Interactions** How does a bill of attainder conflict with the statement that "any person who is suspected or accused of a crime must be presumed innocent until proven guilty by fair and lawful means"?

Grand Jury and Double Jeopardy

5. **Compare and Contrast** Both the grand jury and the writ of habeas corpus protect individuals from unjust imprisonment. How are they similar? How are they different?

6. **Evaluate Explanations** Do you agree with critics of the grand jury who say it is "too time consuming, too expensive, and too likely to follow the dictates of the prosecutor"? Why or why not? Give evidence from the text to support your answer.

7. **Draw Inferences** How does the guarantee against double jeopardy protect an individual's rights?

Going to Trial

8. **Assess an Argument** If the 6th Amendment guarantees a public trial, why do some critics argue that media coverage jeopardizes a defendant's right to a fair trial?

9. **Evaluate Arguments** Did *Gideon* v. *Wainwright* reinterpret the 6th Amendment? Why or why not?

Guarantee Against Self-Incrimination

10. **Draw Inferences** How does the right against self-incrimination support the concept that a person is innocent until proven guilty?

11. **Draw Conclusions** Does the Miranda rule protect a suspect from being held in contempt of court? Explain your answer.

Bail and Preventive Detention

12. **Analyze Information** Would a standard fee for bail that is the same for every person accused of a crime be more or less fair than one set "in accordance with the severity of the crime charged and with the reputation and financial resources of the accused"? Explain your answer.

13. **Evaluate Arguments** Do you agree with the argument that preventive detention undercuts the presumption of innocence? Why or why not? Cite evidence from the text to support your answer.

Cruel and Unusual Punishment

14. Identify Central Ideas The Supreme Court has excluded death by firing squad and by electric chair from the prohibition against cruel and unusual punishment. How does the Court justify this point of view?

Capital Punishment and the Court

15. Compare and Contrast Explain a similarity and a difference between the prohibition against the mandatory death penalty for certain crimes and the prohibition against bills of attainder.

16. Analyze Information Why have most recent capital punishment cases centered on "the application, not the constitutionality, of the punishment"?

Treason

17. **Analyze Interactions** What is the role of Congress and the courts in defining acts of treason and punishing them?

18. **Identify Supporting Details** Why can treason only be committed during wartime?

Lesson 9.1 American Citizenship

Key Terms

citizen	naturalization	denaturalization
jus soli	immigrant	deportation
jus sanguinis	expatriation	

Academic Vocabulary

petition: formal request, application

menial: unskilled, humble, lowly

Lesson Objectives

1 **Describe** how people become American citizens by birth and by naturalization.

2 **Explain** how an American can lose his or her citizenship.

3 **Illustrate** how the United States is a nation of immigrants.

4 **Compare and contrast** the status of undocumented and legal immigrants.

Citizenship in the United States

1. **Vocabulary: Determine Meaning** How are immigrants described in this poem, which is inscribed on the Statue of Liberty? How was immigration changing at the time this poem was written?

> Give me your tired, your poor,
> Your huddled masses yearning to breathe free,
> The wretched refuse of your teeming shore.
> Send these, the homeless, tempest-tossed, to me:
> I lift my lamp beside the golden door.
> —from Emma Lazarus, "The New Colossus" (1886)

2. **Determine Central Ideas** In what two ways can a person become a U.S. citizen?

3. **Explain an Argument** Should U.S. citizenship be considered a right or a privilege?

Natural-Born Citizens

4. **Draw Conclusions** Why was the case of *United States* v. *Wong Kim Ark* so important?

5. **Summarize** As you read "Natural-Born Citizens," use this graphic organizer to record details of the two ways of acquiring citizenship by birth: jus soli and jus sanguinis.

Jus Soli	Jus Sanguinis

Interactive Reading Notepad • Lesson 9.1

Naturalized Citizens

6. **Cite Evidence** About how many immigrants are naturalized in the United States every year?

7. **Explain an Argument** Should citizens by birth have to meet the same requirements as those set for naturalized citizens?

Losing One's Citizenship

8. **Compare and Contrast** Compare and contrast expatriation and denaturalization.

Government Immigration Policies

9. **Use Visual Information** Look at the historical photo of immigrants standing in line at the Ellis Island entry point. The United States is said to be a *heterogeneous* society. What context clues can be found in the photo that show what that term might mean? What is a heterogeneous society?

10. **Use Visual Information** Study the infographic "Immigration by Region." Which were the regions during each time period that the most permanent residents had emigrated from?

11. **Determine Central Ideas** How has U.S. immigration policy changed over time?

12. **Identify Supporting Details** What groups of people are presently excluded from entering the United States?

Government Policies on Unauthorized Immigrants

13. **Cite Evidence** With what current immigration issues does the United States have to deal?

14. Use Visual Information Although it has been illegal since 1987, some employers still hire unauthorized immigrants who are willing to work for substandard wages doing menial work. Use the photograph showing migrant farm workers to define the word *menial*.

15. Integrate Information from Diverse Sources Read the last paragraph of "Government Policies on Unauthorized Immigrants." Then look at the political cartoon. Do the text and the cartoon both tell you the same information concerning immigration reform?

Lesson 9.2 Diversity and Discrimination

Key Terms

heterogeneous
immigrants
reservations

refugee
assimilation

Academic Vocabulary

virulent: bitterly antagonistic; spiteful

Lesson Objectives

1 **Understand** what it means to live in a heterogeneous society.

2 **Summarize** the history of race-based discrimination in the United States.

3 **Examine** discrimination against women in the past and present.

A Changing American Culture

1. **Identify Cause and Effect** Explain the impact that immigration policies can have on the heterogeneous nature of the United States.

Discrimination in America

2. **Assess an Argument** Read this statement by Supreme Court Justice John Marshall Harlan, dissenting in *Plessy v. Ferguson* (1896):

"Our Constitution is color-blind, and neither knows nor tolerates classes among citizens. In respect of civil rights, all citizens are equal before the law. The humblest is the peer of the most powerful."

Taking the perspective of one of the minority groups you have read about that has suffered race-based discrimination in the United States, respond to Harlan's comment. Do you believe that what he says is true? Explain, giving examples.

3. **Compare and Contrast** Study the information provided below. Choose two of the groups to compare and contrast in terms of the discrimination they have experienced. Organize your ideas as a comparison-contrast paragraph.

African Americans	Native Americans	Hispanic Americans	Asian Americans
• slavery • push for civil rights • continued discrimination every day	• driven from lands • forced relocation to reservations • poverty, joblessness, and health issues such as shorter lifespan	• voter restrictions and labor descrimination • deportations • anti-immigrant viewpoints directed at larger Hispanic American groups	• workplace violence • Chinese Exclusion Act • World War II relocation camps

4. **Draw Inferences** How might differences in language, religion, and culture within an ethnic group cause problems as that group tries to obtain equal rights?

Discrimination Against Women

5. **Identify Supporting Details** Efforts to promote women's equality in the United States began in 1848. In 2009, with the Lily Ledbetter Fair Pay Act, Congress took action to try to ensure fair pay for women. What evidence is there that more efforts are still necessary?

6. **Draw Inferences** Why is on-the-job discrimination the most readily identifiable form of discrimination against women?

Lesson 9.3 Equality Before the Law

Key Terms

equal protection

discriminate

rational basis test

strict scrutiny test

segregation

Jim Crow

separate-but-equal doctrine

integration

de jure

de facto

Joseph P. Bradley

William J. Brennan, Jr.

Academic Vocabulary

sanction: to authorize or permit

socioeconomic: social and economic

Lesson Objectives

1 **Explain** the importance of the Equal Protection Clause in safeguarding individual rights.

2 **Describe** the history of segregation in America.

3 **Examine** how classification by gender relates to discrimination.

Equal Protection and Individual Rights

1. **Summarize** Review the paragraph that quotes the 14th Amendment's Equal Protection clause. What does it mean to say that all people must receive the *equal protection* of the laws?

2. **Draw Inferences** Give an example of a law being applied unfairly, in which a person is not receiving the equal protection of the laws.

3. **Draw Inferences** Reread the section about strict scrutiny. Give an example of a situation in which it is reasonable to discriminate against a class of people.

A History of Segregation

4. **Explain an Argument** How did the case of *Plessy* v. *Ferguson* undermine the Equal Protection Clause?

5. **Analyze Sequence** Review the text on *Brown* v. *Board of Education*. Make a list of cases that led up to *Brown* v. *Board of Education*. How did each case pave the way for the decision in *Brown*? What is the overall trend established by these cases?

6. **Compare and Contrast** Review main points of *Plessy* v. *Ferguson* and *Brown* v. *Board of Education* in the text. How does the Court's decision in *Brown* echo the language of *Plessy,* and at what point does it depart from the *Plessy* decision?

7. **Identify Cause and Effect** How can de facto segregation come about without laws that require it?

Gender, Sexual Orientation, and Equality

8. **Assess an Argument** Study the photo that shows male and female students at West Point, and consider what had to happen to get them there. How did equal protection cases dealing with race provide a precedent for cases involving sex discrimination?

9. **Evaluate Explanations** Why do you think the Court has not held *all* sex-based discrimination to be unconstitutional?

10. **Analyze Interactions** What is the connection between the Court's ruling on the Defense of Marriage Act and its decisions in key civil rights cases, such as *Brown* v. *Board of Education?*

Lesson 9.4 Federal Civil Rights Laws

Key Terms

affirmative action

quota

reverse discrimination

Martin Luther King, Jr.

Sandra Day O'Connor

Lesson Objectives

1 **Outline** the history of civil rights legislation from Reconstruction to today.

2 **Explore** the issues surrounding affirmative action.

The History of Civil Rights Laws

1. **Determine Author's Purpose** Study the lesson-opening photo of Dr. Martin Luther King, Jr., again and consider how his actions affected the society around him. What did Dr. King mean when he commented that "Judicial decrees may not change the heart, but they can restrain the heartless"?

2. **Draw Conclusions** Explain how the Serviceman's Readjustment Act of 1944 (the GI Bill of Rights) made a difference to minority groups.

3. **Compare and Contrast** Review the section of text about the Civil Rights Acts of 1964 and 1968. How did each law affect civil rights overall?

4. **Determine Central Ideas** Study the photo of Rosa Parks and its caption. Why did the Civil Rights Acts include not only discrimination based on race or color but also discrimination based on religion, sex, and physical disability?

5. **Analyze Interactions** Consider the section in the text about Title IX of the Education Amendments of 1972. How would you expect this legislation to affect women economically?

Government Policies on Affirmative Action

6. **Assess an Argument** Consider the policy of affirmative action. Does this policy help to redress the effects of past discrimination? Why or why not?

7. **Compare and Contrast** Look at the table of States that have abolished affirmative action at the college level. What is the difference between affirmative action policies that make use of quotas and those that do not? How do quotas change the overall effectiveness of affirmative action policies?

8. **Assess an Argument** Look at the photo of Allan Bakke again, and reread its caption. Supreme Court Justice Sandra Day O'Connor wrote "The Constitution protects persons, not groups. Whenever the government treats any person unequally because of his or her race, that person has suffered an injury." How do Justice O'Connor's words apply to reverse discrimination?

9. **Analyze Sequence** Reread the section of the text about affirmative action cases after *Bakke*. List three major cases in which the Supreme Court has ruled on affirmative action, from 1978 to the present, and explain the overall trend of these cases.

10. **Determine Author's Purpose** What did Justice Sandra Day O'Connor mean when she said, "We expect that 25 years from now, the use of racial preferences will no longer be necessary"?

Lesson 10.1 The History of Voting Rights

Key Terms

suffrage

franchise

electorate

disenfranchised

poll tax

gerrymandering

injunction

preclearance

Martin Luther King, Jr.

Selma, Alabama

Lyndon B. Johnson

John Roberts

Academic Vocabulary

bar: to prevent, prohibit, ban

white supremacist: advocate of the superiority of the white race, racist

compel: to force, require

civilian: any person not an active member of the armed forces or having police power

predecessor: one who goes before, forerunner

dilute: to weaken, diminish, water down

run afoul: to come into conflict with, be at odds with

Lesson Objectives

1 **Summarize** the history of voting rights in the United States.

2 **Identify** the main intention of the 15th Amendment, and describe the results of its lack of enforcement.

3 **Analyze** the impact of political changes brought about by individuals with regard to the civil rights laws enacted in 1957, 1960, and 1964.

4 **Analyze** the provisions and effects of the Voting Rights Act of 1965.

Voting Rights in the United States

1. **Draw Inferences** How have candidates for office had to broaden their campaign messages from the early days of the republic to today?

2. **Summarize** Complete the chart to show how the American electorate has grown from the early days of our nation to the present. The first stage of expansion has been completed for you.

Stage	Dates	How Did The American Electorate Grow?
First	Early 1800s	Religious qualifications eliminated
Second		
Third		
Fourth		
Fifth		

The 15th Amendment

3. **Identify Cause and Effect** The 15th Amendment was ratified in 1870. It was intended to ensure that all African American men could vote. However, Congress did not take any action to enforce the new amendment. What impact did this have on African Americans for the next 90 years?

4. **Draw Conclusions** Why was using the courts to enforce the 15th Amendment not an ideal approach?

Civil Rights Acts of 1957, 1960, and 1964

5. **Compare and Contrast** How did enforcing the 15th Amendment through the Civil Rights Act of 1957 differ from the approach of taking cases to the Supreme Court?

6. **Summarize** Summarize the provisions of the Civil Rights Act of 1964.

Voting Rights Act of 1965–Then and Now

7. **Vocabulary: Determine Meanings** Explain the meaning and intended purpose of preclearance.

8. **Cite Evidence** Why has it been important to continue to amend the Voting Rights Act? Cite evidence from the text to support your answer.

9. **Assess an Argument** What was the Supreme Court's decision in *Shelby* v. *Holder*, 2013?

Lesson 10.2 Your Right to Vote

Key Terms

transients

registration

purging

poll books

literacy

William O. Douglas

Academic Vocabulary

infirmity: physical or mental weakness

fraudulent: deceitful; false

eligibility: qualifications for participation

buttress: to support, reinforce, strengthen

Lesson Objectives

1 **Identify** and explain constitutional restrictions on the States' power to set voting qualifications.

2 **Understand** the criteria for voting in elections.

3 **Understand** the voter registration process and the controversies surrounding voter registration requirements.

4 **Explain** the other requirements that States use or have used as voting qualifications.

Voting Qualifications and the Federal Government

1. **Summarize** Briefly describe who is allowed to vote in this country, based on the five constitutional restrictions on a State's ability to set suffrage qualifications.

2. **Apply Concepts** Beyond the five restrictions you have read about, no State can violate provisions in the Constitution regarding suffrage qualifications. Give an example of a suffrage qualification that would violate a constitutional provision.

Universal Criteria for Voting

3. **Summarize** What are the criteria for voting in the United States, and how have they changed over time? As you read "Universal Criteria for Voting," use this graphic organizer to record information about past and current voter qualifications in the United States.

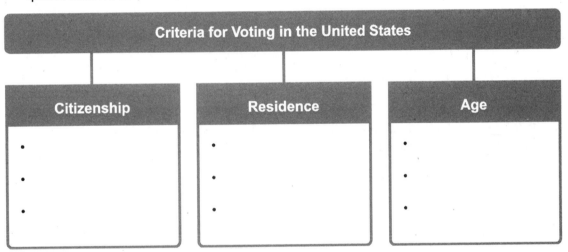

4. **Draw Conclusions** Why do you suppose that more voters who are 65 or older vote in elections than do voters in the 18- to 20-year-old age range?

The Voter Registration Process

5. **Vocabulary: Use Context Clues** Read the first paragraph of the text "Voter Registration Process." What does the word *fraudulent* mean in this paragraph? Do you think voter registration helps election officials prevent fraudulent voting? Why or why not?

6. **Assess an Argument** Read about the controversies surrounding the voter registration process. Consider the views of both critics and proponents of current registration requirements. What can you conclude about voter registration requirements based on the views of both sides?

Historical Criteria for Voting

7. **Identify Cause and Effect** Why did some States enforce literacy requirements as a condition for voting? What caused Congress to eventually ban these requirements? Use evidence from the text to support your answer.

8. **Cite Evidence** What led to the elimination of the poll tax as a condition of voting? Use evidence from the text to support your answer.

Lesson 10.3 Voting Trends

Key Terms

off-year elections

ballot fatigue

political efficacy

political socialization

gender gap

party identification

straight-ticket voting

split-ticket voting

independents

Barack Obama

Donald Trump

Ronald Reagan

George H.W. Bush

Bill Clinton

Academic Vocabulary

facet: side or aspect

alienate: to feel unfriendly or hostile to, isolated from

idolatry: excessive devotion to some person or thing

indifferent: uninterested, uncaring, not concerned

Lesson Objectives

1 **Examine** the problem of nonvoting in the United States.

2 **Identify** the reasons why some people do not vote, and compare these attitudes to those of voters.

3 **Recognize** the sources of information about voter behavior.

4 **Understand** the factors that influence an individual's political attitudes and actions, including voting and voter behavior.

Voter Turnout in the United States

1. **Draw Inferences** Now that you have learned about the origins of the word *idiot*, what can you infer about Greek attitudes toward participating in public life?

2. **Draw Conclusions** What is meant by "off-year elections"? Compare voter turnout in off-year elections to elections in other years.

Why People Do Not Vote

3. **Determine Central Ideas** Why is it true that several million persons who are regularly identified as nonvoters can be more accurately described as "cannot-voters"?

4. **Assess an Argument** What reasons do voters give to defend their decision not to go to the polls?

Influencing Voters and Voting Behavior

5. **Draw Inferences** What are some ways in which the study of voting behavior can impact future elections and the election process?

Sociological Factors and Political Attitudes

6. **Summarize** Complete the chart with one example showing how each sociological factor historically has affected voting.

Sociological Factors Affecting Voting

Sociological Factor	Example of Effect on Voting
Income	
Occupation	
Education	
Gender	
Age	
Religion	
Ethnic Background	
Geography	

7. **Draw Conclusions** Why is it important not to make too much of any one sociological factor when it comes to determining how different groups of Americans will vote?

Psychological Factors and Political Attitudes

8. **Compare and Contrast** What are some arguments for and against voting according to party loyalty? What are some arguments for and against voting independently and considering how each candidate, regardless of party, handles the important issues?

9. **Apply Concepts** The impression a candidate makes on the voters can greatly help or hurt them. How do you think candidates should present themselves to win your vote?

Interactive Reading Notepad

Lesson 10.4 The Voting Process

Key Terms

ballot
absentee voting
coattail effect

precinct
polling place

Academic Vocabulary

legalistic: rule-bound, dry, boring

optical scanner: an electronic system that scans a marked ballot and tabulates votes

electorate: people qualified to vote in a particular region or nation

skeptic: person who questions the validity of a claim or idea

---

Lesson Objectives

1 **Analyze** how the administration of elections in the United States helps make democracy work.

2 **Compare** different methods of filling public offices at the local, State, and national levels, including the role of local precincts and polling places in the election process.

3 **Describe** the various ways in which voters can cast their ballots.

4 **Outline** the role that voting devices play in the election process.

Filling Elected Public Offices

1. **Cite Evidence** The Help America Vote Act of 2002 has had a significant impact on the electoral process. What is this act, and what impact is it intended to have on voters' rights and election outcomes? Use evidence from the text to support your answer.

2. **Draw Conclusions** To what degree did political "machines" have a significant impact on election results? Draw on the text to answer this question.

Precincts, Polling Places, and Ballots

3. **Draw Inferences** How do political parties expect voters to make use of a sample ballot?

4. **Analyze Interactions** Several different groups and individuals manage the local voting process. Identify these officials and their roles.

5. **Summarize** The text describes how voting in the United States has moved from voice voting to unofficial paper ballots to official secret ballots. Drawing on evidence from the text, summarize the reasons for these changes.

6. **Identify Supporting Details** What are the opposing viewpoints about bed-sheet ballots? Include supporting details from the text in your answer.

Casting and Counting Ballots

7. **Determine Central Ideas** Various methods of electronic voting and vote counting have been tried over the years. What drawback(s) do all of these methods have in common?

8. **Summarize** Describe the steps in the process of voting by mail.

9. **Assess an Argument** Complete the chart to show the pros and cons of three ways of voting that might be in your future: in-person voting at polling places, mail-in voting, and Internet voting. After you complete the chart, write a sentence telling which way, or ways, you think voters should be allowed to cast their ballots in the future.

Voting Options	Pros	Cons
In-person voting at polling places		
Mail-in voting		
Online voting		

Interactive Reading Notepad • Lesson 10.4

Lesson 10.5 Public Opinion and Polling

Key Terms

public affairs

public opinion

mass media

peer group

opinion leaders

pundit

mandate

interest groups

public opinion poll

straw vote

universe

sample

random sample

George Gallup

Elmo Roper

Academic Vocabulary

concentrate: to focus on one issue or task

complex: difficult to analyze; having multiple or interrelated parts

socialization: the process of learning a society's values and customs

Lesson Objectives

1 **Examine** the term public opinion, and understand why it is so difficult to define.

2 **Understand** the factors that influence an individual's political attitudes and actions.

3 **Recognize** how polls are used by individuals, political parties, interest groups, or the media to affect public policy and describe the challenges involved in measuring public opinion.

4 **Identify** the steps in the polling process, evaluate the role of the Internet and other electronic information on the polling process, and understand the challenges involved in evaluating polls.

5 **Recognize** the limits on the impact of public opinion in a democracy.

What Is Public Opinion?

1. **Determine Meaning of Words** As you read "What Is Public Opinion," pay particular attention to the term *publics*. What is meant by this term? How do you think the idea of multiple "publics" affects the process of understanding public opinion? Use evidence from the text to support your answer.

Family, School, and Political Attitudes

2. **Identify Supporting Details** What is significant about the fact that "the start of formal schooling marks the initial break in the influence of the family"?

3. **Identify Cause and Effect** As you read "Family, School, and Political Attitudes," use this graphic organizer to list four ways that family and school can influence political attitudes and the effect of each on children.

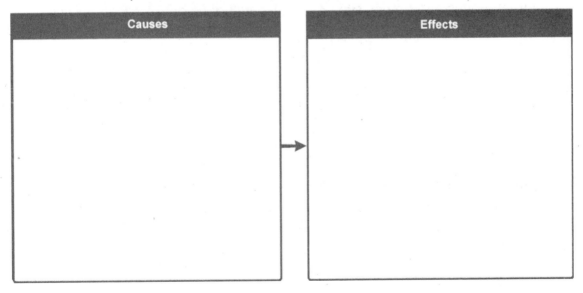

Interactive Reading Notepad • Lesson 10.5

Other Factors That Influence Political Attitudes and Actions

4. **Analyze Interactions** Who has a stronger effect on political attitudes and actions—one's peer group or opinion leaders?

5. **Draw Conclusions** The text describes how historic events, such as the Great Depression and the Vietnam War, have shaped Americans' political opinions. How do you think events of the last decade—for example, changes in economic conditions and communication technology—have changed Americans' political opinions?

Ways to Measure Public Opinion

6. **Vocabulary: Use Context Clues** Use context clues in the text to explain why interest groups are also known as pressure groups. Then tell whether you think interest groups exert a positive or negative influence on American politics.

7. **Analyze Word Choices** The author says that "the media are frequently said to be 'mirrors' as well as 'molders' of opinion." What do the words *mirrors* and *molders* mean in this context? Cite evidence from the text to support your answer.

Public Opinion Polls

8. **Cite Evidence** Certain types of public opinion polls are particularly susceptible to error. Cite evidence from this text to identify which types, explain why this is the case, and describe how pollsters have worked to overcome these issues.

How Polls Are Designed and Administered

9. **Identify Cause and Effect** Following the *Literary Digest* fiasco, what changes did polling organizations implement that led to increased reliance on them, by both the public and political leaders, as a gauge of public opinion?

10. **Draw Inferences** The author notes that the voice and tone of telephone pollsters can impact how an interviewee answers questions. Before telephone interviews were common, pollsters went door-to-door to ask for opinions. What factors might have influenced interviewees' answers to door-to-door pollsters? Draw on evidence in the text to support your answer.

Poll Reliability

11. **Make Generalizations** How much should voters be swayed by the results of public opinion polls when deciding how to cast their ballots? Why?

Lesson 10.6 Influencing Public Opinion: The Mass Media

Key Terms

medium

public agenda

sound bite

Thomas Jefferson

Theodore Roosevelt

Academic Vocabulary

comparative: by comparison

all-pervasive: spread throughout

spawned: produced, brought forth

inclined: more likely, tend toward

hampered: restricted, curbed, limited

Lesson Objectives

1 **Examine** the role of the mass media in providing the public with political information.

2 **Understand** the role played by the mass media in the U.S. political system and give examples of the processes used by the media to affect public policy.

3 **Analyze** the impact of political changes brought about by the media, including the Internet and other electronic information, and understand the factors that limit the influence of the media on the political process.

The Role of Mass Media

1. **Identify Key Steps in a Process** Use this flowchart to record the development of different mass media over time.

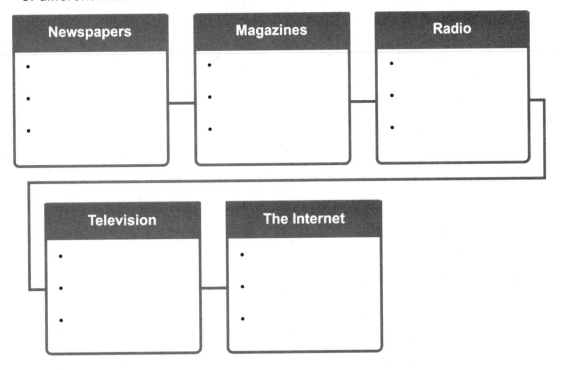

2. **Compare and Contrast** How did the advent of television change how candidates ran their political campaigns? Similarly, how has the advent of the Internet changed how candidates run their campaigns today?

3. **Integrate Information From Diverse Sources** Barack Obama's use of the Internet and social media in both the 2008 and 2012 campaigns has been hailed as a key tool in his successful presidential campaigns. Based on what you have read about the history of the Internet, your personal experiences with the Internet, and any knowledge you have of the Obama campaign, or other campaigns, what Internet strategies do you think are especially effective in political campaigns?

How the Media Affects Politics

4. **Support Ideas With Examples** Explain the media's role in shaping the public agenda. Use a contemporary or historical issue with which you are familiar as an example to support your reasoning.

5. **Compare and Contrast** Use what you have learned from this text to describe at least three ways the media have affected the way candidates run political campaigns today versus 100 years ago.

6. **Use Visual Information** Refer to the "Where Do Americans Get Their Campaign News?" table. Based on the table, where do most Americans currently get their campaign news, and how has this changed throughout history? Use evidence from the table to support your answer.

7. **Draw Inferences** What is the place of the media in a democracy, and how should citizens make use of the media available to them? Use evidence from the text to support your answer.

The Media's Limited Influence

8. **Identify Cause and Effect** This reading notes that most people are more interested in being entertained than informed. What are some of the effects of this attitude on television programming? Use evidence from the text to support your answer.

9. **Cite Evidence** In what way is an article on new fishing conservation efforts in *Field & Stream* magazine an example of how the media's influence is sometimes limited? Cite evidence from "The Media's Limited Influence" reading to support your answer.

Lesson 10.7 Understanding Interest Groups

Key Terms

interest group	lobbyist
public policy	*amicus curiae* brief
public affairs	grass-roots pressures
trade associations	Capitol Hill
labor union	James Madison
lobbying	Alexis de Tocqueville

Academic Vocabulary

pluralistic: made up of several groups with different ethnic, religious, or political backgrounds

elite: select, privileged group in a society

foreboding: an expectation of trouble

mischief: troublesome conduct, misbehavior

commendable: admirable, praiseworthy

reproach: blame, criticism

overt: open, observable

nurture: to foster, encourage, promote

fringe group: a group holding less popular, often extreme views

constituent: one who is represented by a legislator

boon: welcome benefit, stroke of good fortune

Lesson Objectives

1 **Understand** the role played by interest groups in the U.S. political system.

2 **Analyze** the impact of political changes brought about by interest groups, and examine the viewpoints of those who see interest groups as both good and bad for American politics.

3 **Describe** the various types of interest groups in the United States.

4 **Give** examples of the direct approach used by interest groups to affect public policy.

5 **Examine** the indirect lobbying approach and its use of grass-roots pressure, media, propaganda, and political campaigns to influence public opinion and policy.

What Are Interest Groups?

1. **Summarize** Summarize public attitudes toward interest groups, and describe their general role in the American political system.

2. **Identify Supporting Details** As you read, use this graphic organizer to record the positive and negative aspects of interest groups.

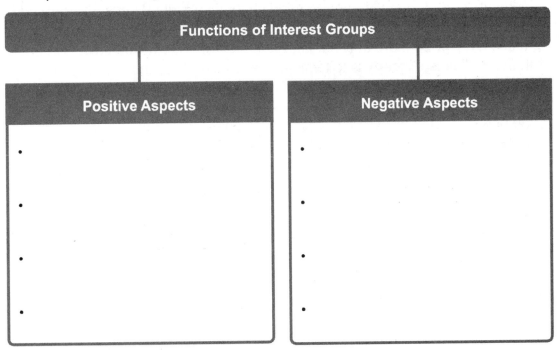

Functions of Interest Groups

Positive Aspects	Negative Aspects
•	•
•	•
•	•
•	•

3. **Determine Author's Point of View** Read the following words from John F. Kennedy, which appeared in "To Keep the Lobbyist Within Bounds" in the *New York Times Magazine* on February 19, 1956:

"Because our congressional representation is based on geographical boundaries, the lobbyists who speak for the various economic, commercial, and other functional interests of this country serve a very useful purpose and have assumed an important role in the legislative process."

How does John F. Kennedy feel about interest groups in the United States? What phrases in the article support your answer?

Different Views of Interest Groups

4. **Determine Author's Point of View** Read the following passage from James Madison's *The Federalist* No. 10, keeping in mind that he uses the word *faction* in place of the term *interest group*:

"It could never be more truly said than of the first remedy that it was worse than the disease. Liberty is to faction what air is to fire, an ailment without which it instantly expires. But it could not be less folly to abolish liberty, which is essential to political life, because it nourishes faction, than it would be to wish the annihilation of air, which is essential to animal life, because it imparts to fire its destructive agency."

Based on Madison's words, how do you think he feels about factions or interest groups?

5. **Assess an Argument** Many people believe that interest groups contribute to the checks-and-balances feature of the political process. Do you agree or disagree with this viewpoint? Explain your reasoning using information from the readings.

6. **Apply Concepts** Consider the following information: Both the American Conservative Union and the Americans for Democratic Action rate members of Congress as "liberal," "moderate," or "conservative" based on how they vote on bills. Based on what you read in this lesson, what valuable function are these interest groups performing?

Why Do Individuals Join Interest Groups?

7. **Summarize** Summarize three reasons why interest groups grew in number in the 1960s and 1970s.

8. **Draw Inferences** How did the media contribute to the interest group explosion in the 1960s and 1970s?

Processes Used by Interest Groups—The Direct Approach

9. **Identify Supporting Details** Identify at least one way in which lobbyists seek to influence each branch of government.

10. **Identify Cause and Effect** Detail the effects of the Abramoff scandal on subsequent lobbyists, including current lobbyists working in Washington, D.C. Use information from the text in your response.

Processes Used by Interest Groups—The Indirect Approach

11. Summarize Summarize four ways in which interest groups work indirectly to influence government and public opinion.

12. Determine Central Issues Using celebrity spokespeople is a common way for interest groups to try to influence policymakers. Do interest groups gain undue influence when celebrities back their causes? Explain.

Lesson 11.1 Political Parties and What They Do

Key Terms

political party

political spectrum

partisanship

single-member districts

plurality

bipartisan

consensus

coalition

ideological

single-issue parties

economic protest parties

splinter parties

ward

precinct

Thomas Jefferson

George Washington

Theodore Roosevelt

Academic Vocabulary

extremist: one on the extreme right or left in politics

rascal: a mean, unprincipled, or dishonest person

cumbersome: unwieldy; clumsy

baneful: troubling, distressing

viable: reasonable, practical, sensible

ideologically: related to or concerned with ideas

smorgasbord: widely varied assortment or collection

agrarian: related to the land or its cultivation

innovator: one who introduces a new approach

divisive: causing disagreement

defy: resist, frustrate

Lesson Objectives

1 **Understand** the origins of political parties in the United States and analyze their major functions.

2 **Understand** multiparty and one-party systems and how they affect the functioning of a political system, and explain the two-party system of the United States.

3 **Evaluate** the role of minor parties that have been active in American politics, and understand why they are important.

4 **Understand** why the major parties have a decentralized structure.

5 **Describe** the national party machinery and party organization at the State and local levels.

What Is a Political Party?

1. **Draw Conclusions** The text defines a political party as "a group of persons who seek to control government through the winning of elections and the holding of public office." Does this definition apply to the Republican and Democratic parties in the United States?

2. **Categorize** Describe the three separate, but closely related, elements that compose the two major American political parties.

The Role of Political Parties

3. **Cite Evidence** Provide an example of a political party performing the following roles: **(a)** nominating, **(b)** informing and activating, **(c)** serving as a bonding agent, **(d)** governing, **(e)** serving as a watchdog.

4. **Identify Supporting Details** Why was the period from the late nineteenth to the mid-twentieth centuries called "the golden age of parties"?

5. **Evaluate Explanations** According to the text, history shows that "political parties are absolutely essential to democratic government." Explain what this statement means.

The Two-Party System

6. **Apply Concepts** In George Washington's 1796 Farewell Address, he warned the new nation against "the baneful effects of the spirit of party." What do you think Washington meant by this comment?

7. **Draw Inferences** What features of the electoral system support the existence of a two-party system?

8. **Use Visual Information** Study the diagram of the political spectrum. Explain the differences between a conservative and a liberal.

9. **Identify Supporting Details** As you read "The Two-Party System" and the following two texts, use this graphic organizer to record details about major and minor parties.

Identify Supporting Details	
Major Parties	**Minor Parties**

Multiparty and One-Party Politics

10. **Compare and Contrast** Compare and contrast two-party with multiparty systems, noting the strengths and weaknesses of each.

11. **Use Visual Information** Study the interactive map of the United States showing the distribution of Republican and Democratic States in 1900 and 2012. From the 1870s into the 1960s, the Democratic Party was dominant throughout the southern States. Which party was dominant in the southern States in 2012? Why do you think this is?

Third and Minor Parties in the United States

12. **Draw Inferences** What type of minor party is likely to develop around the following: **(a)** a strong personality, **(b)** the collapse of the stock market, **(c)** a specific theory about government, **(d)** growing concern about climate change?

13. **Draw Conclusions** State three reasons why a person might wish to vote for a minor party candidate in a presidential election.

14. **Draw Inferences** In what way do minor parties strengthen the two-party system? In what way do they weaken that system? Explain your answer.

The Decentralized Nature of the Parties

15. **Determine Central Ideas** What does it mean to say that the major parties in American politics are decentralized? Would a more centralized political party be more or less effective at winning elections?

16. **Analyze Interactions** What specific situation is most likely to unify a political party?

National Party Functions

17. **Analyze Interactions** Between presidential elections, what does the national committee of each party do?

Interactive Reading Notepad • Lesson 11.1

State and Local Party Functions

18. Draw Conclusions How does party organization contribute to the strength of the two-party system?

19. Use Visual Information Study the diagram of the State and local party organization. What is the largest division shown in the diagram? The smallest?

Lesson 11.2 Nominations

Key Terms, Places, and People

nomination
general election
caucus
direct primary
closed primary
open primary

blanket primary
platform
runoff primary
nonpartisan elections
Ross Perot
Andrew Jackson

Academic Vocabulary

clique: an exclusive group
bedevil: irritate, bother

Lesson Objectives

1 **Explain** why the nominating process is a critical first step in the process for filling public offices.

2 **Describe** self-announcement, the caucus, and the convention as nominating methods.

3 **Discuss** the direct primary as the principle nominating method used in the United States today, and understand why some candidates use the petition as a nominating device.

Nominations—A Critical First Step

1. **Cite Evidence** Read "Impact of the Nominating Process." According to the text, how does the nominating process impact the right to vote in the United States?

2. **Cite Evidence** Read the second paragraph of "Methods of Nomination." According to the text, how do dictatorial regimes impact voting?

3. **Vocabulary: Use Context Clues** Read the third paragraph of "Methods of Nomination." Using what you already know, before reading any further, explain the five ways nominations are made in this country.

4. **Cite Evidence** Read the first paragraph of "Examples of Self-Announcement." Why would someone use the nominating method of self-announcement?

5. **Draw Conclusions** Why might self-announcement attract candidates with the personal wealth to finance their own campaigns?

The Caucus

6. **Identify Supporting Details** Read the quote from *The Works of John Adams (1856)* describing the original caucus. How could this quote be used to support the criticisms of the original caucus?

7. **Vocabulary: Analyze Word Choices** Read the first paragraph of "Criticisms of the Caucus." Explain why Andrew Jackson and his supporters referred to the congressional caucus as "King Caucus."

The Convention

8. **Summarize** Briefly describe how conventions worked at the local, State, and national levels of government.

9. **Identify Supporting Details** How does the quote from R. M. Easley, describing the convention at Cook County (Chicago), Illinois, in 1896, support the fact that conventions were in decline?

Interactive Reading Notepad • Lesson 11.2

The Direct Primary

10. **Compare and Contrast** Read "The Closed Primary" and "The Open Primary." Compare and contrast these two forms of the direct primary.

11. **Analyze Interactions** Read "Versions of the Open Primary." How did California and Washington respond to the Supreme Court's decision in *California Democratic Party* v. *Jones*? How did Louisiana respond?

12. **Explain an Argument** Read "Closed vs. Open Primaries." Which of these two forms of the direct primary do you agree with? Use the text to support your argument.

Evaluation of the Primary

13. **Draw Conclusions** Read the first paragraph of "Other Problems with the Primary." How can the direct primary have an effect on the party itself? Can you think of an example for this?

14. **Draw Conclusions** Read the second paragraph of "Other Problems with the Primary." How might name familiarity be a problem with the primary?

Petition

15. **Draw Conclusions** Why do some States make it more difficult for minor party members or independents to get on the ballot?

16. **Infer** How is filling an appointed office different from filling an elected office?

Interactive Reading Notepad • Lesson 11.2

Lesson 11.3 Electing the President

Key Terms

presidential primary

winner-take-all

proportional representation

keynote address

swing voters

battleground States

district plan

proportional plan

national popular vote plan

Ronald Reagan

Richard M. Johnson

Academic Vocabulary

crazy-quilt: made up of a mixture of things; hodgepodge

vie: to compete with someone to achieve something

loom: to take shape, emerge

quadrennial: occurring every fourth year

barn-burner: an event that is very exciting or intense

culminate: to reach the highest point, climax

standard bearer: a leader of a movement or party

scheme: a plan or system in which things are put together

Lesson Objectives

1 **Describe** the role of conventions in the presidential nominating process, the caucus-convention process, and the events that take place during a national convention.

2 **Evaluate** the importance of presidential primaries.

3 **Examine** the characteristics that determine who is nominated as a presidential candidate.

4 **Describe** the features of the presidential campaign.

5 **Analyze** how the electoral college provides for the election of the President.

6 **Identify** flaws in the electoral college system, and outline the advantages and disadvantages of proposed reforms of the system.

Presidential Primaries

1. **Summarize** What factors led to the adoption of the presidential primary system by the majority of States?

2. **Draw Conclusions** Many of the changes in the nature of presidential primaries are attributed to political party reform efforts. What might that say about the types of candidates voters want to see?

3. **Identify Cause and Effect** In which States are candidates most likely to invest when it comes to dollars spent to get votes?

Evaluation of the Presidential Primary

4. **Identify Supporting Details** Why would presidential primaries be considered "vital," despite the complications of the system?

Interactive Reading Notepad • Lesson 11.3

5. **Compare and Contrast** Using the graphic organizer and information from the text, write a comparison-contrast paragraph about out-of-power vs. in-power presidential primaries.

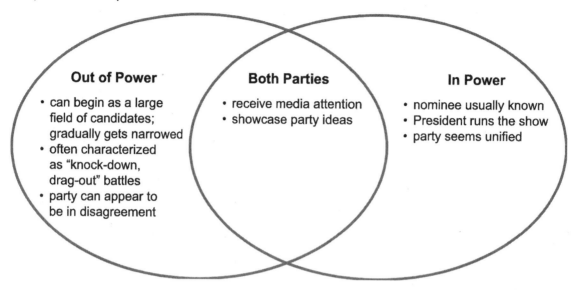

Out of Power
- can begin as a large field of candidates; gradually gets narrowed
- often characterized as "knock-down, drag-out" battles
- party can appear to be in disagreement

Both Parties
- receive media attention
- showcase party ideas

In Power
- nominee usually known
- President runs the show
- party seems unified

The National Convention

6. **Draw Inferences** Why would parties choose to reward some States with extra convention delegates?

7. **Analyze Sequence** Explain why both parties follow the same sequence of events at a national convention.

8. **Integrate Information from Diverse Sources** Use text evidence to support the point that national conventions are full of excitement but lack an element of surprise.

Who Is Nominated?

9. **Draw Conclusions** What career path is a good choice for someone who wants to be elected President one day? Why?

10. **Distinguish Among Fact, Opinion, and Reasoned Judgment** Read this statement: "Ideas about just who is an electable presidential candidate have changed more since 2008 than in the history of presidential elections." Based on evidence in the text, is this statement a fact, an opinion, or a reasoned judgment?

The Presidential Campaign

11. **Paraphrase** Suppose you are a voter living in a battleground State. In your own words, describe what you should expect to experience during a presidential campaign.

12. Use Visual Information Based on the photographs of campaign debates in this lesson, how should candidates try to appear during the debates?

The Electoral College

13. Determine Central Ideas Barring any unusual circumstances, describe the typical outcome of the electoral college during an election.

14. Distinguish Among Fact, Opinion, and Reasoned Judgment Read this statement: "The counting of electoral votes is nothing but a ceremonial duty." Based on what you have learned from the text, is this statement a fact, an opinion, or a reasoned judgment?

Electoral College Scenarios

15. Explain an Argument If the candidate who wins the most popular votes might still lose the election, how do Americans almost always know who the winner is at the end of Election Day?

16. **Analyze Interactions** How might a "faithless elector" be viewed by the Framers of the Constitution?

17. **Draw Conclusions** When partisan politics are prevalent, what are some issues involved in throwing a presidential election to the House of Representatives?

Proposed Reforms and a Defense

18. **Summarize** How do States' rights figure into the electoral college debate?

19. **Paraphrase** In your own words, explain the national popular vote plan.

20. **Explain an Argument** What evidence do the defenders of the electoral college give to support their claim that fears about the system are exaggerated?

Lesson 11.4 Money and Elections

Key Terms

political action committee (PAC)

Super PAC

subsidy

FECA

BCRA

soft money

Federal Election Commission (FEC)

Presidential Election Campaign Fund

hard money

527 organization

John McCain

Russ Feingold

Academic Vocabulary

corrupt: inappropriately influence in return for money or personal gain

Lesson Objectives

Lesson Objectives

1 **Analyze** the impact of campaign spending on the media.

2 **Explain** how campaign contributions by individuals and organizations affect the political process.

3 **Explain** how public funding of candidates affects the political process.

4 **Explain** how campaign finance laws have changed over time.

5 **Distinguish** hard money from soft money.

The Price of An Election

1. **Determine Central Ideas** The text states that the getting and spending of campaign funds can corrupt the entire political process. Explain how this could happen.

2. **Analyze Interactions** What is the biggest expense in a presidential campaign? Why do you think this expense is higher than other campaign expenses?

Where the Money Comes From

3. **Identify Supporting Details** How do politicians pay for political campaigns? Who provides the money to pay for campaign expenses?

4. **Analyze Interactions** How does supporting campaigns with public money, in the form of government subsidies, support the political process in a democracy?

Federal Finance Laws

5. **Draw Inferences** What do you think President Obama meant when he commented that the *Citizens United* case might "open the floodgates for special interests"?

FEC Requirements

6. **Draw Conclusions** How does the FEC protect the political process from corruption by special interests?

7. **Compare and Contrast** How are contributions by political action committees (PACs) qualitatively different from contributions by individuals?

8. **Analyze Interactions** Look at the graph of the top ten PAC spenders in 2016. Why do you think that many PACs contributed both to Democrats and to Republicans?

Loopholes in Finance Laws

9. **Assess an Argument** Do you agree with Senators John McCain and Russ Feingold that the use of soft money to finance campaigns should be limited? Why or why not?

10. **Analyze Sequence** Did the Supreme Court's ruling in the *Citizens United* case affect campaign spending in 2012? Explain.

Lesson 12.1 Types of Economic Systems

Key Terms

capitalism

factors of production

capital

entrepreneur

free enterprise system

free market

law of supply and demand

monopoly

laissez-faire theory

socialism

communism

collectivization

privatization

Great Leap Forward

command economy

Adam Smith

Hugo Chávez

Josef Stalin

Mikhail Gorbachev

Fidel Castro

Mao Zedong

Deng Xiaoping

Academic Vocabulary

just compensation: fair payment for loss

Lesson Objectives

1 **Identify** the factors of production.

2 **Understand** the role played by the National Government in both the public and private sectors of the U.S. free enterprise system.

3 **Understand** the relationship between U.S. government policies and the economy in a mixed economy.

4 **Describe** the four fundamental factors in a free enterprise system and understand how the Federal Government fosters competition and entrepreneurship, as well as how government regulation can serve as a restriction to private enterprise.

5 **Summarize** the theories of Karl Marx, and identify important characteristics of socialist and communist economies and describe socialism and communism in today's world.

6 **Evaluate** the strengths and weaknesses of capitalism versus socialism and communism.

Capitalism and the Factors of Production

1. **Draw Inferences** Could any individual take a series of courses on entrepreneurship and become successful? Why or why not?

The American Free Enterprise System

2. **Explain an Argument** The text states that politics and economics are inseparable. Explain why this is true in a free enterprise system.

3. **Analyze Interactions** Although a capitalist system is said to have four fundamental factors, one of those factors—individual initiative—could be viewed as an essential element of the other three factors. Explain this integrated way of looking at the factors.

What Is A Mixed Economy?

4. **Draw Conclusions** In the United States, why might certain businesses find it in their best interest to operate in one State as opposed to another?

Socialism, Communism, and Karl Marx

5. **Cause and Effect** Consider the ideals behind socialism. Describe the climate that might exist in a country that is ripe for accepting a socialist approach.

Communism

6. **Summarize** To explain why Mikhail Gorbachev insisted on both openness and restructuring, summarize what the situation in the Soviet Union had become as a result of communism.

7. **Draw Inferences** Why has Cuba remained mostly communist?

The Special Case of China

8. **Determine Central Ideas** When countries such as China emerge from communism, they often require foreign investments. Why?

Comparing the Free Enterprise System with Other Economic Systems

9. **Compare and Contrast** At which points on the scale shown below do the following labels belong? Answer by writing each label in the box below its number on the scale.

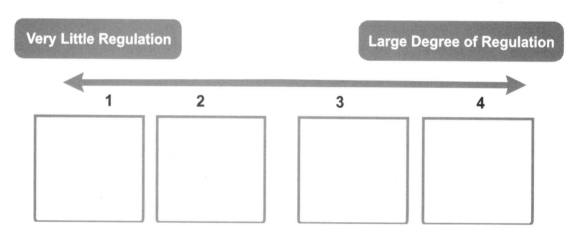

Communism   Laissez-Faire   Mixed Economy   Socialism

Levels of Regulation

Very Little Regulation   Large Degree of Regulation

1   2   3   4

Lesson 12.2 Fiscal and Monetary Policy

Key Terms

gross domestic product

inflation

deflation

recession

fiscal policy

monetary policy

panic

open market operations

reserve requirement

discount rate

interest

Bill Clinton

George H.W. Bush

John Maynard Keynes

George W. Bush

Barack Obama

Academic Vocabulary

fraudulent: false, dishonest

dampen: to deaden or check

tamp: to push down, press

patchwork: something made up of many different parts

prone: likely, subject or liable to

Lesson Objectives

Lesson Objectives

1 **Explain** the major responsibilities of the Federal Government for domestic economic policy.

2 **Describe** the overall goals of the Federal Government's actions in the economy.

3 **Explain** how government fiscal policy influences the economy at the national level.

4 **Explain** how government monetary policy influences the economy at the national level.

Federal Government and the Domestic Economy

1. **Determine Central Ideas** Summarize the role of the Federal Government in the American economy.

2. **Summarize** Describe how three different governmental institutions carry out the role of the Federal Government in the domestic economy.

3. **Use Visual Information** Look at the map of "The Federal Reserve System." Which quadrant of the United States has the most Federal Reserve Banks?

Key Goals for the Economy

4. **Draw Conclusions** What is the gross domestic product (GDP), and what usually happens when the GDP increases at a steady rate?

5. **Identify Supporting Details** What is the Consumer Price Index (CPI), and why is the Bureau of Labor Statistics in charge of reporting it?

How Fiscal Policy Influences the Economy

6. **Identify Supporting Details** As you read "How Fiscal Policy Influences the Economy," use this graphic organizer to record details of how fiscal policy can be used for the two following purposes: (1) to control economic growth and (2) to slow inflation.

To Grow Economy	To Slow Inflation

7. **Cite Evidence** In the midst of the Great Depression of the 1930s, British Economist John Maynard Keynes advocated a two-pronged approach to dealing with the economic disaster. What did Keynes's approach call for the government to do?

How Monetary Policy Influences the Economy

8. **Summarize** What tools are available to the Federal Reserve Board (the Fed) to influence the nation's economy?

9. **Explain an Argument** Which of the tools that is available to the Fed to influence monetary policy might produce the quickest results? Why?

Lesson 12.3 Financing Government

Key Terms

fiscal policy

progressive tax

payroll tax

regressive tax

excise tax

estate tax

gift tax

interest

Benjamin Franklin

Oliver Wendell Holmes, Jr.

George W. Bush

Barack Obama

Academic Vocabulary

levy: to charge, impose

borne: be carried as a burden

grossly: very badly, glaringly

bequest: something left, handed down, passed on

dutied: subjected to a tax by the government

Lesson Objectives

1 **Explain** how the Constitution gives Congress the power to tax and at the same time places limits on that power, as well as, how government taxation and regulation can serve as restrictions to private enterprise.

2 **Identify** the sources of revenue of the U.S. government today, including both tax and non-tax revenues.

The Power to Tax

1. **Determine Central Ideas** Why is the power to tax so important that the Constitution lists it first among the powers of Congress?

2. **Identify Cause and Effect** How does the tax rate paid by individuals affect the nation's economy?

3. **Analyze Interactions** How does collecting taxes from businesses affect the nation's economy?

4. **Summarize** Explain how it is possible for the same corporate profits to be taxed twice.

5. **Draw Inferences** Why is it important that the Federal Government not be able to tax State governments in the exercise of their proper governmental functions?

Federal Taxes Today

6. **Draw Conclusions** Suppose that an individual wants to continue earning income but does not want to pay any taxes at the end of the year. How could an individual accomplish this goal?

7. **Categorize** Why can payroll taxes be considered a form of social welfare?

8. **Evaluate Explanations** How does the power to tax affect the business community?

9. **Analyze Interactions** How do regressive and progressive taxes affect people of different economic classes?

10. **Evaluate Explanations** Does it work for government to try to discourage certain behaviors, such as smoking or drinking alcohol, by imposing a "sin tax"? Why or why not?

Lesson 12.4 Spending and Borrowing

Key Terms

entitlements

controllable spending

uncontrollable spending

continuing resolution

deficit

surplus

demand-side economics

supply-side economics

public debt

Panama Canal

Herbert Hoover

Franklin D. Roosevelt

Ronald Reagan

George Washington

Academic Vocabulary

stoke: feed, stir up

binding: imposing an obligation or duty

stimulate: encourage, spur, whip up

accrue: to increase in value or amount over time

ceiling: upper limit

Lesson Objectives

1 **Identify** government expenditures and define controllable and uncontrollable spending.

2 **Analyze** the executive branch function of creating the federal budget, in conjunction with Congress.

3 **Understand** the relationship between U.S. government policies as set out in the yearly federal budget and the economy.

4 **Analyze** the impact of Federal Government sources of revenue and expenditures on the U.S. economy.

5 **Analyze** the causes and effects of the public debt.

Federal Expenditures

1. **Cite Evidence** What are entitlement programs? List three examples of those government programs.

2. **Compare and Contrast** What is the difference between controllable and uncontrollable spending?

3. **Vocabulary: Use Context Clues** Why is controllable spending sometimes referred to as "discretionary spending"?

4. **Identify Supporting Details** As you reread "Federal Expenditures," record notes in this graphic organizer about the top four federal spending priorities.

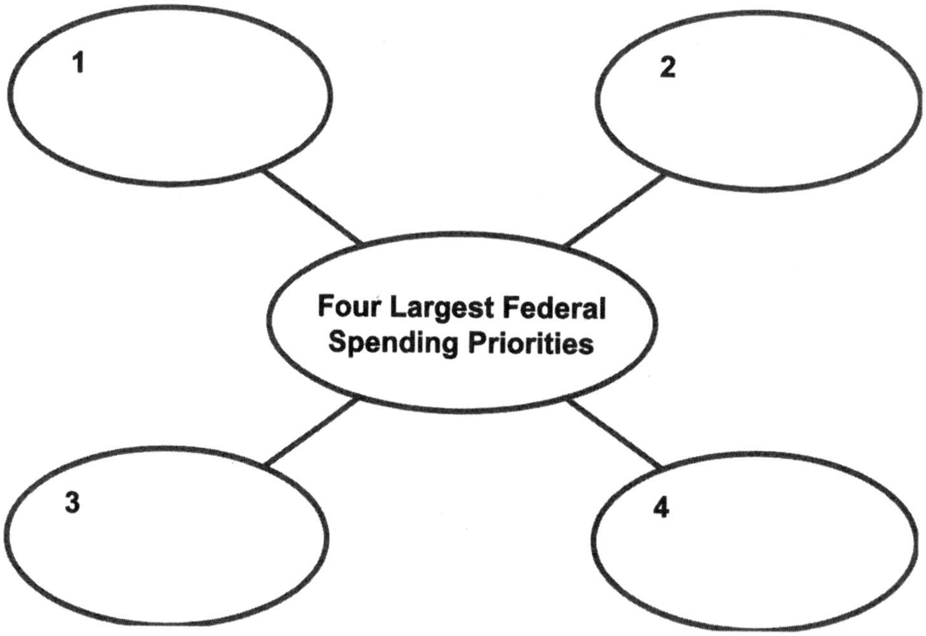
1
2
Four Largest Federal Spending Priorities
3
4

Creating the Budget

5. **Vocabulary: Use Context Clues** What is the purpose of a continuing resolution?

6. **Identify Key Steps in a Process** What is the President's role in the budget-making process?

7. **Identify Key Steps in a Process** What is Congress's role in the budget-making process?

Borrowing and the Deficit

8. **Identify Cause and Effect** How does the Federal Government borrow money? Does anyone benefit from this borrowing system or is anyone disadvantaged by it?

9. **Identify Supporting Details** Why can the Federal Government borrow money at a lower interest rate than private investors can?

10. **Draw Conclusions** How could the United States create a budget surplus?

Understanding the Public Debt

11. **Determine Central Ideas** What is the public debt?

12. **Draw Conclusions** Is concern over the size of the public debt justified? Why or why not?

Interactive Reading Notepad

Lesson 12.5 The U.S. in a Global Economy

Key Terms

protectionism

tariff

import quota

trade embargo

North American Free Trade Agreement
(NAFTA)

International Monetary Fund (IMF)

World Bank

World Trade Organization

Group of 8 (G8)

globalization

Academic Vocabulary

interdependence: dependence upon one another

hallmark: distinguishing feature

tangible: real, physical, touchable

instantaneous: happening in an instant

Lesson Objectives

1 **Explain** the causes of globalization, including recent scientific discoveries and technological innovations, and its effects on the American economy, including why certain places or regions are important to the United States.

2 **Understand** the roles of the executive and legislative branches in setting international trade and fiscal policies.

3 **Identify** international trade organizations and alliances to which the United States belongs.

4 **Recognize** the benefits and drawbacks of the global economy, including the significance to the United States of the location and key natural resources of particular countries.

5 **Understand** world economic trends today.

A Global Economy

1. **Determine Central Ideas** What are the advantages for the United States to trade with other countries?

2. **Analyze Interactions** How can you predict a country's most likely trading partners? Include the United States as an example in your answer.

U.S. Trade Policies

3. **Compare and Contrast** Compare and contrast tariffs and import quotas. What are the advantages and disadvantages of each for the United States?

4. **Cite Evidence** List at least three examples of industries in which both domestic producers and international businesses are thriving.

5. **Explain an Argument** What arguments are made by those who support NAFTA (the North American Free Trade Agreement)? What arguments are made by those who oppose it?

Trade Alliances and Organizations

6. **Summarize** What is the purpose of trade organizations, such as the WTO (World Trade Organization) and the Group of 8?

7. **Analyze Interactions** Why do countries need regional trade alliances as well as global ones?

The Consequences of the Global Economy

8. **Determine Central Ideas** What risks are involved in international trade?

9. **Identify Cause and Effect** What is a trade deficit, and how does a trade deficit affect the United States?

10. **Draw Conclusions** How has the role of the United States in the international marketplace changed over time?

Interactive Reading Notepad

Lesson 13.1 The California State Constitution

Key Terms

separation of powers
checks and balances
popular sovereignty
limited government

initiative
fundamental law
statutory law

Academic Vocabulary

subordinate: less important

plague: to disturb, negatively affect

miscellaneous: varying; not belonging to a single category

obsolete: out of date

Lesson Objectives

1 **Examine** the underlying principles of the first State constitutions.

2 **Describe** the history of the California constitution.

3 **Examine** California's current constitution

4 **Explain** the process for constitutional change in California and elsewhere.

The First State Constitutions

1. **Compare and Contrast** As you read "The First State Constitutions," use this graphic organizer to compare and contrast what you know about the United States Constitution with features of the State constitutions.

The Federal Constitution versus State Constitutions

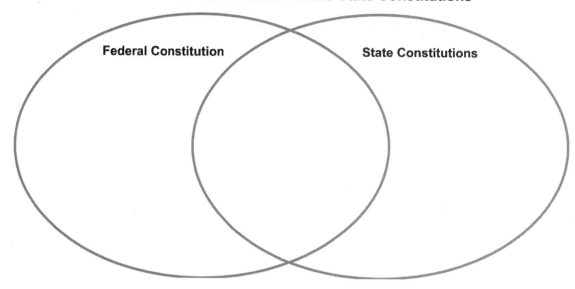

2. **Identify Central Issues** What change did the State of Massachusetts bring to the process of constitution-making?

History of the California Constitution

3. **Identify Cause and Effect** Explain how California's early efforts to support its railroads led to constitutional change in the State.

4. **Cite Evidence** The text says: "As a result of these changes, California government is a blend of representative and direct democracy." What changes does this statement refer to? When were these changes made, and why?

The California Constitution Today

5. **Identify Supporting Details** What rights does California's constitution protect in addition to those listed in the Bill of Rights found in the United States Constitution?

6. **Infer** Why do you think most States cover the subject of governmental structure in very specific detail in their State constitutions?

Constitutional Change

7. **Compare and Contrast** What are the three ways in which Californians can propose constitutional amendments? What are the benefits and drawbacks of each method?

8. **Draw Inferences** Why do you think that many State constitutions remain unnecessarily lengthy and detailed and have so many outdated provisions?

Lesson 13.2 The California Legislature

Key Terms

police power

constituent power

initiative

referendum

Academic Vocabulary

nonpartisan: not belonging to or favoring any political party

impeachment: the process of bringing formal charges against a public official

turnover: rate at which people enter and leave a group

Lesson Objectives

1 **Explain** how the work of the California legislature affects citizens' daily lives.

2 **Compare** the structures and function of California's legislative branch with the legislative branch of the Federal Government.

3 **Describe** the election process, terms, powers, and organization of the California State legislature.

4 **Summarize** how a bill becomes a law in California.

5 **Analyze** the initiative and referendum as vehicles for political participation.

Structure and Size

1. **Assess Arguments** Evaluate the arguments for bicameral versus unicameral state legislatures. Which position do you think is stronger?

2. **Draw Conclusions** In what ways is California's legislature similar to and different from other State legislatures?

Qualifications and Election

3. **Identify Supporting Details** How do primaries in California differ from those in most other States? Why do you think California adopted this system?

4. **Analyze Information** How did the *Baker* v. *Carr* and *Reynolds* v. *Sims* decisions affect California?

Powers of California's Legislature

5. **Make Generalizations** What is the police power? Give an example of a California State law based on the police power.

6. **Identify Central Issues** How do the nonlegislative powers of the California legislature illustrate the principle of checks and balances?

Organization

7. **Hypothesize** What might be the advantages and disadvantages of term limits for State legislators?

8. **Compare and Contrast** Identify two ways in which the speaker of the California assembly has more power than the president of the California senate.

The Lawmaking Process

9. **Explain** What are the different sources of bills in California?

Direct Legislation

10. **Draw Conclusions** What form of the initiative is used in California? Do you think California should allow citizens to vote on ordinary laws through the initiative process? Why or why not?

11. **Support Ideas with Evidence** Do you think that initiatives and referendums are effective ways for voters to influence or control government? Explain your thinking with evidence from the text.

Lesson 13.3 California's Governor and Executive Branch

Key Terms

gubernatorial

recall

line-item veto

clemency

pardon

commutation

reprieve

parole

Academic Vocabulary

intangibles: things not concrete or easily defined

fragmented: split; separated into many pieces

reluctant: hesitant; unwilling

Lesson Objectives

1 **Describe** the qualifications, selection, and term of California's governor.

2 **Summarize** the governor's roles, including the powers, duties, and limitations of the office.

3 **Examine** the duties and powers of California's attorney general.

4 **Describe** the other California State executive offices.

The History of the Governorship

1. **Analyze Information** Explain why separation of powers between individual State governors and the legislature "proved unsatisfactory" in the early days of the American republic.

Overview of the California Governorship

2. **Explain an Argument** Why might the authors of California's constitution have set only minimal qualifications for the governorship? What additional qualifications would you expect in a governor?

3. **Hypothesize** Why do you think many other States elect the governor and the lieutenant governor as a team? What are some advantages and disadvantages of this method of choosing top State executive officers?

4. **Compare and Contrast** How is the California governor's role similar to the presidency? How is it different?

The Governor's Executive Powers

5. **Analyze Interactions** What checks and limits are placed on the governor's appointment and removal powers in California?

6. **Identify Steps in a Process** What role does California's governor play in creating the State budget?

Legislative Powers

7. **Draw Conclusions** What is meant by the "message power?" How can the governor use this power?

8. **Interpret** How can the governor use his or her veto powers to limit State spending?

Judicial Powers

9. **Compare and Contrast** What clemency power does California's governor lack? Who exercises this power in California?

Other Executive Officers

10. **Identify Patterns** California's governor shares the executive powers with other elected officials. As you read this text, use a two-column notes format to record the responsibilities of each of California's elected executive officers.

11. **Identify Supporting Details** What facts support the statement that, in California's executive branch, the governor is "first among equals"?

Interactive Reading Notepad • Lesson 13.3

12. **Compare and Contrast** How is the position of California's lieutenant governor similar to that of the Vice President of the United States? How is it different?

13. **Draw Conclusions** Among the executive officers of California's State government are the attorney general, the treasurer, the superintendent of public instruction, the controller, and the secretary of state. Which of these officials most affects your daily life? Which do you think has the most important job? Explain your answers.

Interactive Reading Notepad

Lesson 13.4 California State Courts

Key Terms

common law
precedent
criminal law
felony
misdemeanor
civil law

justice of the peace
warrant
appellate jurisdiction
jury
information
preliminary hearing

Academic Vocabulary

compelling: powerful

probate: the official proving, verifying of a will

backlog: a build-up of unfinished work

summon: call, send for

verdict: decision or judgment

Lesson Objectives

1 **Identify** and define the kinds of law applied in California State courts.

2 **Analyze** the various levels and responsibilities of courts in the federal and State judicial systems and the relationships among them.

3 **Describe** the jury system in California.

4 **Compare** the role of judges at the State and federal levels with other elected officials.

5 **Examine** the different ways that judges are selected.

Text 1: Types of Law

1. **Summarize** What is common law, and what are its origins?

2. **Draw Conclusions** Why do you think common law remains important to our legal system?

3. **Use Visual Information** Look at the flowchart titled "The Use of Precedent." What is the significance of the arrows pointing downward from the middle row of cases to the ruling?

4. **Compare and Contrast** How are criminal and civil law different?

California's Court System

5. **Draw Inferences** Which of the types of courts in the State judicial system of California would you expect to be the most widely used? Explain your answer.

6. **Categorize** What are the special departments of the superior courts? How is it decided which cases go to a special department?

7. **Draw Conclusions** What are the benefits of a unified court system?

The Jury System in California and the Nation

8. **Identify Supporting Details** As you read "The Jury System in California and the Nation," use this graphic organizer to record details of the two basic types of juries in the American legal system—the grand jury and the trial jury (also known as the petit jury).

Types of Juries	
Grand Jury	**Petit Jury**

9. **Draw Inferences** Most government processes in this country must take place in public, but a grand jury does its work in secret. Why do you think this is?

Interactive Reading Notepad • Lesson 13.4

10. **Explain and Assess an Argument** What are the main drawbacks or criticisms of the jury system? Assess one of these issues.

California and Other State Judges

11. **Explain an Argument** How do you think judges should be selected? Choose one method described in this text and create a strong, well-supported argument for that method.

12. **Identify Supporting Details** What qualifications do you think a good judge should have? Write a help-wanted advertisement for your ideal candidate.

13. **Draw Conclusions** How does the Missouri Plan for selecting judges use both appointment and election?

Lesson 13.5 Local Government in California

Key Terms

county

charter

ordinance

special district

township

municipality

incorporation

mayor-council government

strong-mayor government

weak-mayor government

council-manager government

zoning

metropolitan area

Academic Vocabulary

constable: local police officer

purse strings: financial resources

prescribe: to order, set down, specify

woe: problem

Lesson Objectives

1 **Describe** county government and the ways it affects citizens' daily lives.

2 **Examine** the unique position of tribal governments in the United States.

3 **Consider** the role of towns, townships, and special districts.

4 **Compare** the major forms of city government.

5 **Evaluate** the need for city planning and list some major municipal functions.

6 **Outline** the challenges that face suburbs and metropolitan areas.

Counties Across the Nation

1. **Determine Meaning of Words** Provide an overview of the term *county,* using examples from the text to help define the term as it applies to States across the United States.

County Governments in California

2. **Draw Conclusions** What advantages do charters bring to charter counties? What kind of county is likely to adopt a charter?

3. **Summarize** Summarize the structure and role of California's county boards of supervisors.

Local Governments Outside of California

4. **Compare and Contrast** How are counties in some New England States different from counties in California and across much of the rest of the nation?

Cities, Towns, and Urban Living

5. **Explain** What impact has the population shift from rural to urban areas had on local governments? Draw from the text to support your answer.

6. **Describe** What role does a charter play in city government?

What Do Cities Do?

7. **Integrate Information** In what ways does city government affect the daily life of a high school student? If you live in a city, give examples from your life.

Forms of City Government

8. **Summarize** Cities across the United States use several forms of government. Drawing from the text, summarize the most important aspects of those forms of government in a table-style graphic organizer.

Most Common Forms of City Government		
Characteristics of Each Form		

9. **Analyze** How might a council-manager form of government positively and negatively affect a city that uses it?

Interactive Reading Notepad • Lesson 13.5

City Planning

10. Identify Supporting Details What details in this text support the idea that most American cities developed "haphazardly," with "no eye to the future"?

11. Support Ideas with Examples Give examples of conflicts or problems that zoning ordinances are intended to avoid.

Suburbs and Metropolitan Areas

12. Cite Evidence Explain the consequences of "suburbanitis" and sprawl, citing evidence from the text.

Other Forms of Local Government in California

13. Make Generalizations What kinds of issues prompt governments to form special districts?

14. Analyze Information How are California schools governed?

Tribal Government

15. Summarize What does it mean to say that recognized Native American nations have a "government-to-government" relationship with the United States?

Lesson 13.6 Spending and Revenue in California

Key Terms

Medicaid

welfare

entitlement

sales tax

regressive tax

income tax

progressive tax

property tax

assessment

inheritance tax

estate tax

State budget

Academic Vocabulary

tuition: fee paid for schooling

entitled: eligible for, qualified to receive

recipient: one who receives

arbitrary: unfairly determined by chance

contrived: carefully planned, skillfully designed

exemption: freed, excused from a duty

enterprise: initiative, drive, determination

Lesson Objectives

1 **Examine** State and local spending on education, public health, public safety, transportation, and the environment.

2 **Describe** the constitutional and other limits on taxation.

3 **Identify** major tax and nontax sources of California State and local revenue.

4 **Summarize** the State budget process.

California State and Local Spending

1. **Integrate Information** As you read this lesson, use the graphic organizer below to record information about the services California's State government provides and the sources of its revenue.

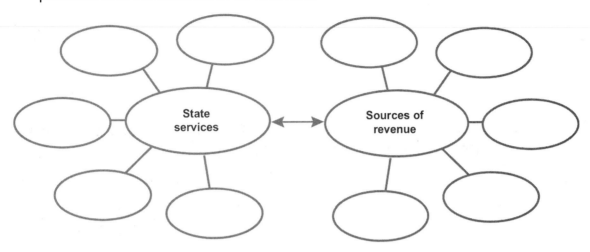

2. **Cite Evidence** Refer to the text as well as the graphic "California State and Local Spending" to cite evidence supporting the following conclusion: The education of California residents is one of the State's highest priorities.

3. **Identify Supporting Details** In what ways does the State government work to improve the health and welfare of Californians?

Interactive Reading Notepad • Lesson 13.6

4. **Make Generalizations** Are transportation services best provided by State governments or the Federal Government? Use specific information from the text to support your answer.

5. **Use Visual Information** Study the diagram "Malibu Public Beaches Guide." How does the information support the California Coastal Commission's mission?

Taxation: Principles and Limits

6. **Hypothesize** Examine the diagram "Adam Smith's Four Principles of a Sound Tax System." Why do you think Adam Smith argued that paying taxes should be convenient?

7. **Summarize** Describe the State and federal constitutional limits on taxation.

Sources of California State Revenues

8. **Hypothesize** Why do you think California collects a higher proportion of its revenue from sales tax than the national average?

9. **Evaluate Data** Study the chart "California State and Local Revenues." What are California's primary sources of revenue? In what way do the revenues generated from these sources reflect the overall economic climate?

10. **Draw Conclusions** Examine the map "Property Taxes by State." How might you explain why property taxes in Modoc County are so much lower than property taxes in Marin County?

Interactive Reading Notepad • Lesson 13.6

State Budgets

11. Compare and Contrast How are the operating and capital budgets of California similar? How are they different?

12. Identify Key Steps in a Process Outline the steps in the creation and passage of California's State budget. Why is it called an executive budget?

Lesson 14.1 Democracy and the Changing World

Key Terms

democratization

hard-liners

reformers

Lech Walesa

Nelson Mandela

Aung San Suu Kyi

Mikhail Gorbachev

Boris Yeltsin

democratic consolidation

failed states

Academic Vocabulary

undermining: secretly weakening

dissent: disagreement with an official opinion

coalition: a group joined for a common purpose

Lesson Objectives

1 **Examine** how regimes can make transitions to democracy.

2 **Analyze** why some countries experience setbacks or failed transitions to democracy.

3 **Explain** the factors necessary for democratic consolidation to take place.

4 **Describe** democratic change and continuity in selected countries today.

Text 1: Transitions to Democracy

1. **Draw Inferences** Explain why the role of reformers is important in a dictatorship.

2. **Draw Conclusions** Why is democratization such a vital step in a country's transition to democracy?

Text 2: Examples of Transitions to Democracy

3. **Use Visual Information** Refer to the text and the timeline "Germany's Path to Democracy." What are some factors that had to develop for East Germany and West Germany to successfully reunite?

4. **Determine Central Ideas** Explain why Mikhail Gorbachev is considered a reformer instead of a hard-liner. Then describe how he helped the Soviet Union to change.

5. **Assess an Argument** Vladimir Putin was instrumental in the passage of legislation mandating that those who participate in demonstrations can be fined heavily—in amounts exceeding a year's salary for many Russians. Some people use this fact to argue that Putin is leading the Russian government toward authoritarian rule. Do you agree or disagree with this argument? Explain your reasoning.

Text 3: Outcomes of Transitions to Democracy

6. **Identify Key Steps in a Process** How might the United States help other countries build strong, independent democratic institutions?

7. **Use Visual Information** Refer to "What Makes Democracy Succeed?" Which of the factors listed do you think is the most important for a democratic system of government to take root and flourish? Explain your response.

Text 4: Democratic Change and Continuity Today

8. **Draw Inferences** Consider the Middle East and Egypt's struggles as they transition to new governments. How can religious and linguistic divisions pose challenges for a government in transition?

9. **Cite Evidence** How has Egypt moved farther away from democracy instead of toward it? Cite evidence from the "Democratic Change and Continuity Today" text in column 1 of the graphic organizer to support your answer. In column 2, explain why the evidence you provided in column 1 supports the idea that Egypt is moving farther away from democracy.

Cite Evidence	Explain Evidence

Lesson 14.2 The United Kingdom

Key Terms

constitutionalism

parliamentary system

coalition

ministers

shadow cabinet

common law

devolution

backbenchers

party government

Academic Vocabulary

sovereignty: a country's right to govern itself

bicameral: having two branches or chambers

heredity: inheritance of title, office, or right

polarization: a sharp division into opposing factions

Lesson Objectives

1 **Explain** the United Kingdom's legacy of constitutionalism.

2 **Outline** the structure of government in the United Kingdom.

3 **Examine** public policy and elections in the United Kingdom.

4 **Compare** government in the United Kingdom with that of the United States.

A Legacy of Constitutionalism

1. **Compare and Contrast** How did democracy come about in the United States compared to the United Kingdom?

2. **Use Visual Information** Look at the map of the United Kingdom and read the text. Describe the country's primary geographical feature and explain how it has affected the formation of the United Kingdom's government.

Government in the United Kingdom

3. **Identify Supporting Details** Describe the features of the United Kingdom's Parliament.

4. **Determine Central Ideas** How does a coalition work in the United Kingdom's government, and why is it necessary?

5. **Summarize** Complete the graphic organizer to show how the government of the United Kingdom is chosen and organized.

Official Institution	How Chosen?	What Role or Powers Does This Person/Group Have?
Prime minister		
House of Commons		
House of Lords		
Cabinet		
Monarchy		

Public Policy and Elections

6. **Compare and Contrast** According to the text, the winning party in Parliament creates and carries out policy with overwhelming party loyalty based on the party's platform. How is this similar to and different from the United States Congress?

7. **Identify Cause and Effect** In the United States, elections tend to be candidate-centered, while in the United Kingdom, elections are party-based. How does the structure of each government play a role in how elections are carried out?

Comparisons to the United States

8. **Categorize** What is the difference between a federal system of government and a unitary system of government? Use examples from the reading to support your answer.

Lesson 14.3 The Russian Federation

Key Terms

Vladimir Lenin

Josef Stalin

purge

Vladimir Putin

Academic Vocabulary

hierarchical: organized by order or rank

dissolution: the process of ending an organization

referendum: a public vote on a particular issue

decree: an official order

bolstered: strengthened, supported

Lesson Objectives

1 **Examine** Russia and its history since the Bolshevik Revolution.

2 **Outline** the structure of Russia's government.

3 **Examine** how public policy is created in Russia.

4 **Compare** government in Russia with that of the United States.

Russia and Its History

1. **Summarize** Describe the actions of Vladimir Lenin and Josef Stalin and their impact on the government of Russia.

2. **Draw Conclusions** What were the most significant events that contributed to the formation of the Russian Federation and its transition to a democratic republic?

3. **Identify Supporting Details** What details under "Reform Led by Gorbachev" support the idea that the transition to a democratic Russian Federation was not easy?

Government in the Russian Federation

4. **Compare and Contrast** How are the offices of the United States Vice President and the Russian Federation Prime Minister alike? How are they different? Use information from the text to support your answer.

5. **Identify Supporting Details** Describe the elements of the Russian executive branch that contribute to the nature of government in the Russian Federation.

6. **Use Visual Information** Look at the "Organization of Russian Federation Government" chart. Write a description of the Federal Assembly, comparing it to the United States Congress.

Public Policy Creation

7. **Use Visual Information** Look at the image of the Udmurtneft oil field. Explain the significance of this image and the impact of this and similar scenarios on the presidency of Vladimir Putin.

Comparison to the United States

8. **Compare and Contrast** As you read "Comparison to the United States," use this graphic organizer to compare and contrast the governments of the United States and the Russian Federation.

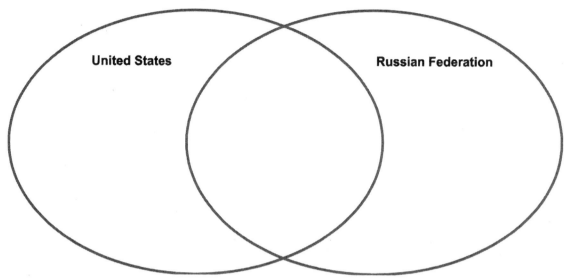

Lesson 14.4 China

Key Terms

Cultural Revolution

Mao Zedong

Chiang Kai-shek

Deng Xiaoping

Academic Vocabulary

autonomous: having the power or right to govern itself

fervor: a strong feeling of excitement and enthusiasm

provisional: likely to be changed

fundamental law: basic law of a government as opposed to legislative acts

privatization: removing from government control and placing under private ownership

---

Lesson Objectives

1 **Examine** China and its history starting with the birth of the People's Republic.

2 **Outline** the structure of China's government.

3 **Examine** how public policy is created in China.

4 **Compare** government in China with that of the United States.

China and Its History

1. **Draw Inferences** Under Mao Zedong's leadership, teachers and intellectuals were bullied, and artists and scholars were sent away to farms. Why was this done, and how did it help Mao pursue his Cultural Revolution?

2. **Draw Conclusions** What did Deng Xiaoping and his government demonstrate to the Chinese people at Tiananmen Square?

Government in China

3. **Determine Central Ideas** The Communist Party has 82 million members, which only translates to about 6 percent of the Chinese public. How is the Communist Party still in power?

4. **Analyze Interactions** Why is the United States in the awkward position of being officially pro-Taiwan but also recognizing the status of the People's Republic of China?

Comparing China and the United States

5. **Compare and Contrast** Complete the first two columns of the chart to show how the role of the media has been the same and different in China under Mao Zedong and today. Then, add information from the text and your own general knowledge to show the role the media plays in the United States.

Role of Media during Cultural Revolution	Role of Media in China Today	Role of Media in U.S. Today

Interactive Reading Notepad • Lesson 14.4